STEAM
IN MY FAMILY

John Newton

Foreword by R.A. Whitehead

MERESBOROUGH BOOKS
1988

Published by Meresborough Books, 17 Station Road, Rainham, Kent. ME8 7RS
Meresborough Books has published over one hundred books about Kent and a few on Sussex. In addition they publish a monthly magazine, 'Bygone Kent', founded in 1979, available from newsagents and bookshops in Kent or by postal subscription. Full list of books sent on request.

ISBN 0948193 417

Printed by Dotesios Printers Ltd, Bradford-on-Avon, Wiltshire.

CONTENTS

To My Father
WILFRED EDWARD NEWTON
1901-1980
A giant amongst MEN OF STEAM

FOREWORD

Fifty years ago, when the use of steam vehicles on the road and on the farm was in decline, the study of them and of their history was confined to a very small number of individuals, some of whom, incidentally, banded together in 1937 to form what is now the Road Locomotive Society. Since then the study of the subject, apart from the set-back of the war years, has made great progress, a by-product of which has been the appearance of over fifty books on this or related topics. In addition there has been the rise of the traction engine rally, from small, and sometimes frivolous, beginnings in the early 1950s to its present scale. This, in turn, has helped to provide both a reading public for the books that have been written and a recruiting ground for the national and local societies which now cater for those interested in the subject.

John Newton has qualifications for joining the band of authors on more than one score. On the one hand he is a prominent figure in the rally and preservation movement being an engine owner and Chairman of the Thames Valley Traction Engine Club. On the other, he comes from a family in which three generations were involved closely in the ownership and working of traction and ploughing engines in Romney Marsh. What he has set out to record is the life of those three generations of Newtons and of the group of villages in which it was set, mainly, but not exclusively, as seen through the eyes of his father, Wilfred Newton. To this narrative he has added notes on the engines they owned. I am not aware that this has been attempted on this scale before. I found it interesting to read and am honoured to have been asked to contribute the foreword.

During the period of the story arable farming was in almost continuous decline and his grandfather and great grandfather must have been in almost continuous battle against intense competition on rates, against slow payers and the difficulties of managing with ageing equipment. Despite this underlying trend of the slow running down of arable farming, the story is predominantly one of contentment and modest satisfaction, of plain meals eaten with relish and rest enjoyed after real weariness. In short it is a pleasant work, conceived in filial respect and completed in many hours of patient work.

I wish it well.

R.A. Whitehead
January 1988

Tonbridge, Kent

5

ACKNOWLEDGEMENTS

I acknowledge with gratitude the invaluable assistance I have received from a number of individuals during the compilation of this work, amongst whom are many friends and relations. In naming the following I crave the forgiveness and indulgence of any that I have omitted in error.

My thanks go to: H.J. Clark, A.J. Martin, the late A. Huggett, the late T.B. Paisley, A. Duke and L. Burberry of the Road Locomotive Society, D. Phillips of The Institute of Agricultural History, Museum of English Rural Life, University of Reading, R.E. Hooley, of Ruston Gas Turbines Ltd, T. Olive of Aveling Barford Ltd, A.W.F. Smith of the Steam Plough Club, B.G. Thomas of the Kent County Council Archives Office, E.W.G. Dredge for photographic assistance.

I would especially like to thank the surviving brothers and sisters of my father and their respective spouses, who have tolerated my many questions with calmness and a sympathetic ear, and who time and again have told me some of the detail contained in these pages. Special thanks go, therefore, to Mrs D. Jemison, the late Mrs M. Newton, the late Mrs G. Offen, Mr and Mrs J.T. Maddock, Mr and Mrs R.E. Newton, Mrs S. Ward and to my cousin and her husband Mr and Mrs G.H. Cottington.

To Derek B. Stoyel, undoubtedly the greatest living authority on the steam engines that worked in Kent, goes my heartfelt thanks, not only for his friendship but for all the work he has done on my behalf. He has meticulously searched his extensive records to help bring authority and accuracy to my engine detail, and has been instrumental in tracing some of the rare photographs contained herein.

Robert A. Whitehead, the famed author, lies in a special category as regards my gratitude. He has besides kindly writing a foreword to this work, given me unstinting help not only with my text and historical detail, but has given freely of his time and talents. His efforts have gone beyond those occasioned by friendship, and are acknowledged by me with immense gratitude.

Last but by no means least I thank my daughter-in-law Kathleen who has so skilfully typed my manuscript. I pay tribute to and thank my wife Brenda and my immediate family for all their encouragement which made this somewhat difficult task worthwhile.

INTRODUCTION

With the death of Wilfred Edward Newton at Hungerford in Berkshire on 23rd October 1980 at the age of 79 years, one of the last major links with the steam ploughing and threshing contracting firm of E. Newton and Sons of Brookland, Kent was severed.

It is as a tribute to the memory of my father and to his outstanding skill as a steam engine driver that I am prompted to write these words. For the true men of steam, through the passage of time, are now becoming very thin on the ground. I feel it right and proper therefore that those of us who fantasize about what it was really like and play with engines at rallies should not forget the harshness of the times and the men that formed the heritage that we so dearly crave to cling to.

Many of these stories, amusing, hard and sometimes cruel were told and retold by my father upon my many requests as a small boy. Others have been gleaned from many sources in more recent years, but all from whatever source relate to my family. They portray I feel a very real look into the past. They give a true mirrored reflection of the social and economic conditions that prevailed at the turn of the century, and for a few years beyond. Days before the Welfare State was even dreamed of, when to work was of paramount importance, for it brought with it money for food. Without work there existed penury, hunger and the workhouse, and all such evil sounding words and situations that we try to forget in these enlightened times.

During the last decade or so I have endeavoured repeatedly to find time to recall these stories, and to record for posterity the part played by my family in this our small sphere of history.

Unfortunately, what with a growing family and their needs and the pressures of trying to build up a business this was never achieved. Latterly when I did have more chance unfortunately my father's recollections were not so clear, and therefore with his passing it is with some urgency now that I endeavour to set down these happenings whilst they are still fresh in my mind.

John L. Newton
Hungerford

January 1988

7

Chapter 1

IN THE BEGINNING . . .

Great-grandfather Edward Newton was a native of Hinxhill, a small village situated a few miles from the market town of Ashford in Kent, lying just off the main road to Folkestone. The year of his birth was 1852.

I know little of his early life, save that he courted and married a young lady of similar age to himself, named Julia Sutton. I believe Julia's father to have been a foreman of one John Sankey, an ironmonger from Ashford who was also a supplier of agricultural equipment and an agent for steam engines for his locality.

What I do know, however, is that by the time of the birth of their first child — my grandfather, Walter Edward — on 23rd February 1878, they had set up home at 'The Black House' in the neighbouring village of Brabourne. This house was so named because, like many others in an area close to the sea, it was tarred on the windward side in an effort to make it weatherproof.

Sometime between that date and the turn of the century they had moved to Wittersham, on the Isle of Oxney, a village on the borders of Sussex, some five miles from the ancient cinque port of Rye.

It is at the Poplars Farmhouse that my story really begins, a house typical of that part of the country, square fronted, part tiled under a tiled roof, having a chimney each end, lying adjacent to and set some few yards distant from the main road that passes through the village. It was whilst living there that Edward Newton founded the steam ploughing firm that bore his name, and about which this book is written.

I can only assume that very little land went with the Poplars Farmhouse, possibly an odd paddock or two and obviously a farmyard where his equipment was stored when not in use.

Grandfather Walter spent his early life at Wittersham where, in company with his three brothers and three sisters, he not only attended the village school but also in due course helped his father, working in his business. He was therefore, even if not by birth, in most senses a 'Wittersham Boy'.

Those early days of the firm must have been busy for Edward, for we find that his services were being asked for over an increasingly wide area. This was

Opposite: My most prized photograph, taken at Harvey Farm, Brookland in 1905, is of Fowler engines Nos. 3365 and 3197 8 NHP of 1877. Standing in front with his hand on the toolbox is the firm's founder, my great-grandfather Edward Newton, together with his eldest son, my grandfather Walter. In turn his eldest son, my father Wilfred then aged 4 years, stands by his father. Also in the picture are Edward's son Fred and his daughter Grace. — Photo believed to have been taken by Maj. R.J.W. Ind.

(Copy from the collection of H.J. Clark)

undoubtedly due to a number of factors, not the least being that his was one of the very first sets of steam ploughing tackle to operate in that area. As his business grew he found that an increasing proportion of his work came from the Romney Marsh, which resulted in the tackle being used more and more a good distance, sometimes twenty miles, from home. This extensive fertile plain lent itself much more easily to the steam plough than did the undulating, predominantly small fields of the more established farmsteads of East Sussex. Large tracts of land now came under the plough, and as his fame spread so did he find the centre of his operation shifting even further away from Wittersham.

His son spoke often of his long march every Monday morning, starting long before daybreak, to walk down into the marsh to wherever the ploughing engines were at work. Again on the following Saturday afternoon he would walk home for the weekend.

Many times on these journeys they would walk together, father and son, with their flag baskets hanging on their backs in which all their essential food for the long week ahead would be carried. These flag baskets were woven from hessian, with webbing handles, through which a short rope was passed, this when slung over the shoulder and held at the front helping to make lighter work of this cumbersome bundle.

The distances covered on foot, by men employed in all manner of occupations in those days, seem almost beyond comprehension to us accustomed to readily available mechanical transport. It is a fact, however, that such walks took place frequently, and the persons involved would gauge their departing time from home by the distance they had to cover, making sure always to be at their place of work by the recognised starting time of the job in hand. The stories about these treks are legion.

It was, in fact, on such a journey as this that a conversation between my grandfather and his father took place, which was to alter the events about which I write.

Leaving work on the engines one Saturday afternoon at a farm in the parish of St Mary's — one of the many parishes on the Marsh which though small boasts a fine church through the benefaction of the wealthy medieval wool merchants — the two men set out to walk home to Wittersham.

Even though they took as many as they could of the innumerable footpaths that crisscrossed the countryside at that time and walked in as direct a line as possible, their journey was a long one. I would estimate around 20 miles!

My grandfather at this time was a young man in his teens, and as they were crossing a farm he remarked that he was tired. This was not surprising after a heavy week's work. His father said that they were not even half way home yet and that he must plod on, to which his son replied that he wished that they lived on this farm, as it was on the Marsh and it would suit them better. This struck home forcibly to his father who agreed with him and said that they would keep an eye on it and make some enquiries as to the likelihood of this happening. The place was The Harvey Farm, Brookland.

It was around this time that grandfather in turn met, fell in love with and married my grandmother Emily Eliza (née Williams), who was engaged as a children's nurse at The High House, on the Isle of Ebony. The Isle of Ebony, like the Isle of Oxney, had been an island before the recession of the sea and the subsequent draining of the Marsh land.

They were married in the tiny church at Ebony in 1900 but by the time they set up their first home the family had moved again, this time down into the Romney Marsh to Brookland, for Harvey Farm had become vacant and they leased it from the Mortimer Estates at Sittingbourne.

For a few months, there being only one dwelling at Harvey, the farmhouse itself, the newlyweds lived in one of a row of very small houses, known as Alma Cottages, Back Street situated right in the village, and reached by a small lane which runs alongside the church wall.

Within a short space of time, however, Edward was able to rent the field across the road from the farmstead together with a dwelling house known as Elm Cottage into which his eldest son Walter and his new bride moved. These were leased from the trustees of a Miss Green, and eventually purchased from them by Edward on 16th October 1905, the business being conducted by the firm of Hallett, Creery and Co., Solicitors of Ashford.

The newlyweds set up home in this small house of brick and tile close by the narrow lane that was set at right angles to and a quarter of a mile distant from the more major road, exactly opposite which was situated the homestead and buildings of the farm.

It was there on 4th March 1901, as the dying embers of the Victorian era faded, that my father Wilfred Edward was born, he being the eldest son of the eldest son who was in years to come, to play a major part in the life and times of this respected family of agricultural contractors.

11

Chapter 2

EARLY DAYS

Father's early childhood, like that of so many of his contemporaries, was mundane, but not uneventful. Unfortunately he suffered severely from asthma which, before the coming of the modern drugs that helped him in later life, meant that his early days were often painful and distressing.

Schooling was in the village school some three quarters of a mile further along the lane from his home, and was administered by a Governess — Miss Allgrove. By all accounts she was a formidable lady, who never learned that my father was a proud person, like the horse that would not be driven but could more easily be led. I am told by my mother, who was a year younger than he but attended the same school, as did all the village children sharing one large classroom, "the Governess would knock the education into you". She found solace from her toils in the bottle concealed about her ample person. This bottle, sometimes also kept in a locked cupboard, when empty would often be given to my mother to take to the local hostelry for replenishment. Upon its presentation to the innkeeper, he would instantly recognise it, and know from whom it came and with what it had to be refilled. One can only guess at what my maternal grandfather would have had to say about all this if he had found out, he being a staunch chapel man, a lay reader and, besides, a severe and strict disciplinarian.

Given the right leadership and encouragement my father would undoubtedly have got along well at school, having a bright mind, as my mother recalls, but this was not to be, for upon being late for school some days, for a variety of reasons, from having, for instance, to do errands for his mother or, as often was the case, through being so ill with asthma that he could hardly breathe — the Governess would say — "and why are you late again Newton?" to which he would reply "The asthma, Miss", whereupon she would taunt him about 'The asthma', and beat him for being late or absent. Sometimes, even before his tenth birthday, he would have to go for a day or two as cook boy to one of the ploughing gangs, much to the annoyance of Miss Allgrove.

His schooldays ended with his having possibly only two claims to fame, one for being the boy most often chastised by the Governess, and the second, and much more important, for being the boy who threw the school bully into the ditch. This ditch which ran close by the school, and still does, was crossed by a narrow footbridge with handrails on both sides. The inevitable happened one day, and a confrontation took place between the bully, resplendent in waistcoat

A Brookland school photograph c.1915. The author's mother is the third girl from the left in a large hat. This was probably taken during her last term at school.

13

'Shammy' Bottle's shop at the end of Brookland High Street. It was demolished circa 1950 to make way for road improvements on the A259 T road which passes through the village.

with a watch on a chain, and my father who refused to move aside or go back. In the resultant struggle the bully, much larger than my father, ended in the ditch, much to the glee and rejoicing of the rest of the school. He used to tell that the beating he got from the Governess for fighting that day was worth every stroke.

Often after school was over for the day he would have to go back to the village shop for some items for his mother, to feed the family, growing not only in size but in number. By the time he reached 25 years of age he was the eldest of eight. The village shop was, by all accounts, a most marvellous place open all hours selling everything imaginable and run by a man named Mr Bottle, commonly known as Shammy.

Because of these numerous visits to Mr Bottle's establishment and the old fellow taking a liking to him, he offered my father the job of errand boy. I suspect father's desire to earn some pocket money not forthcoming from home and with the prospect of the odd tit-bit thrown in, made him keen on the idea and he took the job.

This was a big step up in his young life, for not only had he got a proper job, albeit only after school week days and on Saturdays, but Mr Bottle owned a delivery bike. This he had to master, which he soon did, and became so expert at it that his dexterity eventually led to his downfall.

He recalled many happy hours spent at the shop, often weighing up flour, sugar and the many items that today come pre-packed but in those days sold

14

loose. Mr Bottle and his staff were kind to him, and it was in the warmth of this kindly atmosphere away from all the pressure of the family life and of his mother trying to cope, as always, on too little income that his character developed.

He told of many trips around the villages, delivering goods and groceries, often in the dark after school, with only the light of an oil lamp to help, despite which these were often happy times for him.

The Romney Marsh of Kent where Brookland is situated is in the main below sea level and is drained by many small and large ditches, or dykes as the inhabitants call them. Most fields are not bounded by hedges but by these variously sized dykes, which serve admirably as barriers for the famed and predominant local breed of sheep.

Footpaths as in all rural communities crossed these fields and dykes, and this by means of a single plank of wood. Where the dyke was wide there would possibly be a handrail but anything less than 10 to 12 feet wide would have nothing but the plank. In winter when the dykes were full, the water often lapped over the planks or, if not, the motion of walking on the planks would cause them to bounce and slap the water.

Returning to Mr Bottle's deliveries, there was an occasion when my father was armed not only with a full basket of groceries in the carrier at the front of the bike, but with an early accumulator on one handlebar and a can of paraffin on the other. In a hurry to finish and having crossed this plank many times before, albeit in daylight, he took the short cut at speed. The result, I am sure you can imagine — he did not come off — rather the plank bounced with the weight of bike and rider in a hurry and the paraffin slopped out all over the groceries. Back to Mr Bottle! This was the first major mishap. All again went well for sometime but worse was to come.

I talked earlier of his dexterity at riding the bike. One busy day he was delivering groceries and was in a hurry to finish. Loading the bicycle as usual he carried a further basket of provisions on his arm, as he had done many times before, making one journey to two customers. Again coming to a wide dyke with the traditional plank, but this time with the handrail on one side as support, he rushed along and down the slope towards the plank, only to realise too late to stop, that for some reason which he always maintained he could not understand, he had got the basket on the wrong arm, on the side of the handrail. Somehow I do not recall hearing much more about Mr Bottle and his shop after this episode!

During all this time — his early schooldays and young life — his favourite playground must have and would naturally have been the farmyard and workshop down the road. His every spare moment during weekends and school holidays found him running down the lane, alongside the familiar dyke, to where by the roadside in turning it resembled a pond, which as I recall was always full of rushes and pokers and with moorhens and dabchicks swimming and nesting.

As he ran he looked to see if the wisp of smoke was rising from the forge chimney and listened for the sound of the click click click of the blacksmith's hammer.

Across the road on the grass, just inside the fence facing the gate in due season the engines stood in a long line, poised to take to the road again after their winter's rest. All were Fowler ploughing engines — dating back to the 1870s. Arranged around and behind them were the other pieces of equipment which were so necessary to the family's trade and survival — ploughs, cultivators, living vans, water carts and so on. All these items that were like magic to so young a boy he would soon come to know intimately.

The buildings housing the blacksmith's forge and workshop, barns and cattle yards lay on the right of the row of engines as he looked at them and these in turn separated the large yard cum stack yard, saw yard, and general dispersal area from the farmhouse where his grandparents lived. This house was eventually to be his home for many years as upon the death of the firm's founder, Edward, his father took him and his mother and family to live there.

The blacksmith's shop in those days seemed to have been his favourite hunting ground. The blacksmith, David Cottington, was, by all accounts, a great friend of his — a genius with a hot piece of iron who could turn his hand to anything. David served the family faithfully for a great many years. Dad enjoyed his company immensely and often recalled listening intently to the tales of his fascinating life abroad as a soldier, told in the warmth of the blacksmith's forge whilst the large man ate his lunch, amidst all the tools of his trade, with the acrid smell of sulphur from the fire mingling with the smell of the dust on the earth floor, and the inevitable covering of dust and cobwebs over all, from the years of busy and painstaking work. Dad recalled how he used often to pump the bellows of the forge, and also got Dave — as he was known by all — to make him little things to play with, all the time keeping a wary eye out for his father.

Many years after the last fire had gone out in this forge I visited it many times and would stand and gaze around — my nostrils and senses reeling, as my whole being tried to take in the very completeness of this building, silent and dark now, not only without life and clatter, but blackened by the years of smoke and toil. Somehow I could not help feeling, that here I was in a different world as an onlooker, but rightfully so, as it was all so much a part of my very own existence. Great work, from replacing a few boiler tubes to much more complicated repairs, must have been done in this building and its adjacent workshop, made large enough to accommodate a complete ploughing engine under cover. All was done with the minimum of tools and the skill of the blacksmith, his strong hands and steady eye.

I felt I was truly standing in the footsteps of my father and his father and grandfather before him. I could easily picture that small boy pulling on the bellows handle and chatting excitedly to the blacksmith, glistening with perspiration from his labours.

Chapter 3

COOK BOY

As soon as the frost of winter gave way to less severe conditions the engines and tackle, duly repaired, refurbished and repainted as necessary, would prepare to leave, for there was much work to be done in the season that was just starting. The steam ploughing engine was responsible for breaking up into cultivation vast areas of marshland that hitherto had not been tilled as with only horses in use up to that time not much cultivation had been done. Permanent pasture for sheep had been the order of the day. It is interesting to recall that the firm was responsible for ploughing large areas of land today occupied by holiday camps and chalet homes, all along the sea wall at Dymchurch and St Mary's Bay, and also putting under the plough land at Old Romney, New Romney, Newchurch, Ivychurch and areas adjacent to Dungeness around Lydd on Sea.

As in most contracting businesses then or now, they had regular customers to whom they returned each season, sometimes more than once as required by the dictates of cropping, but they were also breaking new ground and taking on new farmers as their business expanded. Most villages in the Romney Marsh were familiar with the sight of their equipment as also were many folk in the uplands across the military canal, and into the neighbouring county of Sussex.

When all was ready and they were prepared to move off the news spread around the village that 'Newton's engines are out'. What a sight it must have been. Coming out into the road and turning right, they formed a row, a half mile long completely filling the road side from the farm to the main road — to the pinnock crossing (a little bridge under the road). This was the sight that was so common to my father as a boy, and one in which he was soon to play a major role.

Each ploughing gang consisted of two engine men and two ploughmen who steered the engines whilst on the road. The order of travel was for the foreman of the outfit to take his engine first with the plough coupled to it, followed by the second engine bringing the living van, cultivator and water cart. The farmer to whose premises they were going was responsible for providing the labour and horses for hauling the water to the engines as well as supplying coal.

Besides the men already mentioned there was one other person on each gang — to my mind the unsung hero of his day — the cook boy.

Leaving school, I suspect gladly, at 13 years of age, just as the Great War was beginning, my father was to become a cook boy for a few seasons. The rigours of this life were already known to him, for even from such an early age as nine he had had to fill in as-it-were for a few days — sometimes during school term to the displeasure of the school mistress and also for a week or two during the

17

school holidays. But with schooling behind him he had no chance of escaping from what I believe was in its own sphere virtually slave labour.

The role of the cook boy was more than the name implies. His task was to look after the men, and live with them in the van from one week end to the next. The normal week for a ploughing gang started from first light on Monday when upon arriving at the site of the job in hand the engines were lit and work started as soon as steam was raised, and went on from daylight to dark each day until mid-day on Saturday, when the engines were cleaned out, blown down, refilled and prepared for the following week's work.

During all this time the cook boy was expected to be the provider of all things needed to ensure a smooth running outfit. His tasks started in the mornings by washing up and clearing away the crockery that the men had used upon waking, as it was their custom to start work at first light, then break for breakfast around eight o'clock. By this time the fire in the van had to be bright and the breakfast of eggs and bacon and the inevitable tea well on the go.

After breakfast his job would entail cleaning the van and doing any shopping necessary for the men. Finding out what was wanted: loaves of bread, bacon, potatoes, eggs, milk, beer, tobacco, candles, paraffin and so on, and then walking to the nearest shop to obtain these items. Sometimes this might be a mile or two away, depending upon where the gang was working as not every small community boasted a local shop. My father often told of this trudge, in heavy boots, with a clean sack slung over his shoulder in which to carry his purchases. Often potatoes and eggs could be persuaded out of the farmer or his wife, with sometimes apples for baking thrown in. Then it was back to the van to cook up the kettle (my father always referred to boiling a kettle as this) and take a jug of tea out to the men, working invariably further away from the van. This was the equivalent of elevenses. The van was usually parked on waste land in the corner of the field or on some similar odd site. Consequently as the work progressed, the engines moving along the headland with the plough, the distance the cook boy had to walk to reach the men always increased. It does not need much imagination to visualise the rough walking involved along a headland travelled by the engines and water cart in boots all the time made heavier with the clinging soil. After refreshing the nearest engine driver and the ploughmen, the boy had to travel to the farthest engine — for each man had to be treated alike. Curiously during all the time as a cook boy and later as an engineer my father never recalled the men having their tea out of cups or mugs but always out of small pudding basins. The cook boy would, therefore, be armed on these excursions with a large can of tea and one basin which would serve all concerned in turn, returning afterwards to the van to make sure that the potatoes were cooked and all would be ready for the hastily eaten lunch.

Again after clearing up after the meal the main task of the afternoon would be to ensure that sufficiently large quantities of clean water were brought to the van, often from the well at the farmyard, which naturally meant many journeys to and fro with buckets and pails.

Mid afternoon would find the cook boy again armed with his tea can paying a further visit to his crew, but this time his heart would be light. For from now until dark he would have the rest of the day to himself. It was after this tea round that he often was allowed his reward for his day's labours — a ride on the plough or a stand on the engine — and there is no doubt whatsoever that most of the generations of steam ploughmen first learned their trade and became enslaved to their craft from these times spent whilst a cook boy.

The cook boy's brief respite over he had to return to the van to ensure that come knocking off time, when the engines would be banked down for the night — by which time it would be dark — the van would be prepared for their return. The fire had to be specially bright with large quantities of hot water ready for them to wash off the day's grime in a bucket outside before devouring their meal prior to turning in for the night.

My father recalled many times that living in such close proximity to hard and strong men for long periods at a time was not, as it might seem at first glance, a horrifying or traumatic experience, but rather, with only a few exceptions, the reverse. There existed a very strong bond of brotherliness, comradeship and pro-tectiveness towards one another that he found did not exist in many other spheres of life. In their hard way these men of a few words were very fond of their cook boys but of course they would not allow their feelings to show, let alone speak their praises aloud. These ploughing gangs, who travelled their respective territories, were tight knit communities of their own — having by their own resourcefulness to meet their problems and overcome all their difficulties as they presented themselves. This is one reason why I am sure that the ploughing engine men always felt they were one cut above the rest of the agricultural com-munity. Also this feeling was engendered in them by the feeling of awe with which their fellow countrymen used to look upon them. Seeing them travelling through their villages, in charge of their vast machines, stopping a few days and moving on, maybe they felt that the tedium of their ordinary humdrum lives did not descend on these men of steam, but the plough men themselves would have told them differently. The main difference, however, was that by dint of their long hours of toil and sheer hard work they did at least have some money in their pockets which often was not the lot of the ordinary farm worker or village boy.

Returning to the cook boy, his day ended tired out, he would retire to his bed, the top bunk at the back of the van. It is a strange thing to relate that my father slept well in these conditions, high up under the roof of the van in the warmth from the fire, safe in the company of his mentors. The atmosphere was good for his chest and his asthma seemed bettered for it. Sheer exhaustion of a young body might also have had some part in the reasons for his slumbers.

During the seasons he spent as cook boy, he invariably did not travel with his father's gang, but mostly with that of his uncle. The engines in this gang, as all the firm's engines, were early Fowler single cylinder types, dating back to the 1870s.

It was during his time as a cook boy that many events happened that were to stay fixed in my father's mind for the rest of his life. I feel they also illustrate quite clearly the times and contemporary attitudes, harsh by today's standards but commonplace in the first decades of this century when conditions for all were hard. Moreover, if his stories make it seem that life was severe for those engaged in steam ploughing then how much harder was the lot of the hourly paid labourer and his family? Attitudes towards their own kin were seemingly harsh and cruel, but it must not be forgotten that these hard worked men had little time for the niceties of life. Their task was simply to work hard whilst they had the opportunity in order to feed and clothe their families. Their clothing might have been rough and their food a basic staple diet based on potatoes, bread, fat bacon and beer when they could get it, but at least for the most part they had work — they were, in fact, the lucky ones. These were the good times for them, which unhappily were not to last for many more years to come, the seeds of the depression and end of the era of steam were being sown even then — the small clouds were beginning to gather over the horizon. These conditions and situations were to affect my own family as disastrously as any other, but of the time of the present of which we write a few more years of relative peace and prosperity were still to come.

On one occasion the ploughing gang were working a good distance from Brookland, out beyond Wittersham their original home. During the latter part of this particular week the weather broke and it became virtually impossible to carry on ploughing until Saturday mid-day, the farmer demanding that they should cease. Therefore a hasty stop was made late on the Friday afternoon much to the chagrin as well as, in a way, the relief of the men — for all work was conducted on a piece work basis and to stop meant less income for the week. However the men decided to break on the Friday and hope that by Monday morning things would have improved. After the usual cleaning up of the engines, and a wash and brush up for the men, they decided — my father's uncle amongst them, as foreman of that particular gang — to go home that evening and make a longer weekend of it than usual — which would be a welcome break.

Whereupon they set off, some on their bicycles, leaving my father, as a boy not having one, to remain, saying to him, as he remembered quite well in later years, "you will be alright boy" and "see you Monday morning".

With the disappearance of the gang and only the gradually quieting engines for company, my father settled down in the van for the night, a boy alone in a man's world. He recalled that as the night wore on he became increasingly uneasy, as would be natural, and by the time the first grey light of dawn appeared he was on his way, having decided that the prospect of two more nights alone in

Opposite: 'The family connection'. For a time my mother's eldest brother Fred Apps worked as a cookboy for the Newtons. Here he is shown with his tea caddy in his hand. Engine No. 3365 2nd November 1877 8 NHP KE 6251. — Photo believed to have been taken by Maj. R.J.W. Ind.   (Copy taken from the collection of H.J. Clark)

the van in a strange and lonely situation were not for him. He clearly remembered taking an orange with him for sustenance on the journey and striding out for home.

It was well into the afternoon of the Saturday when he crossed the yard of Harvey Farm, taking a direct route to his home a few more hundred yards away. He was sighted and stopped by the firm's founder, his grandfather, a man of rough square stature, with a full black beard, who had a soft spot for his first grandchild. He said "Hello Billy — where have you come from?" to which my father replied "Wittersham, Grandad." The old man was astounded, and asked to be told all about this incident. As he listened his anger grew and finally he said "What in those boots?" my father's boots, being heavy with hob nails and very worn out. Whereupon he took the tired boy into the farm house and his grand-mother, a kindly soul and a true victorian lady of starched collars and crisp black long dresses, who would never walk to Church on Sunday, but had to be driven in the Governess Cart, made him a hasty meal. He had eaten his orange before the day had hardly dawned, and a milk drink, as he told me, was very welcome. Before leaving for home he was assured by his grandfather that "I will have a word with your father about those boots." He remembered then being tucked up into bed that night and sleeping as he had never done before, and a new pair of boots duly were his the next week. The journey home had been nineteen miles!

Another incident bearing some similarity to this happened when again my father was left alone in the van for the night. The van at that time was parked alongside a dried up dyke, the other side of which the small country road ran by.

The night was brightly moonlit and my father struggled to get to sleep, with the piercing eerie light casting strange shadows around the inside of the familiar van. Sleep was not easy that night, even the exertions of a long day as cook boy did not seem to help his slumbers, but he was determined not to let fear and the scorn of his companions upon their return get the better of him.

Waking after one fitful burst of sleep, he was sure he had heard a strange noise, a sort of bellow — but felt it could not have been. Certainly it was not a cow. He recalled jumping out of his bunk and lighting a candle for comfort. His hearing was straining, his hair beginning to stand up on the nape of his young neck and then he heard it again, but this time it was a different noise, gradually getting louder, a kind of muffled scuffing noise, and the noise grew — scuff — scuff — scuff. He could contain himself no longer. Determined to meet his tormentor — if he had to meet him — face to face, at least in the open, where any way he might have room to run, he silently as he could slid back the bolt on the van's stable door, and dropped to the ground. What he saw startled him even more. Passing along the road was a strange shape, the moonlight glistening on the back of this leviathan, this creature from a different world, or if not world then continent. It was an elephant, being led along the road, belonging to a circus that was going to Rye. It was customary in those days to walk the large animals from one venue to another. Nevertheless this was a sight that was so imprinted upon his mind that every facet of that night was to remain crystal clear to him during the whole of his life.

Many times during those years that he was cook boy incidents happened that were not only frightening but amusing, such as the time when the van was parked on a bit of waste ground at the rear of this particular farmyard and adjacent to the field in which the ploughing was taking place. The buckets of water he placed under the van kept being emptied or knocked over. He was unable to find out why until he discovered that a donkey whose patch this piece of ground presumably was either drank them dry or through his innate curiosity knocked them over whilst the labouring cook boy was fetching some more in readiness for the men's wash up at the end of the day. Not all happenings were as easily dismissed or forgotten as this though.

The last incident that I relate in this chapter concerning my father's spell as a cook boy was of a more serious nature. It illustrates well the danger that always lurks, and is associated with, the working of heavy machinery. These dangers, ever present, are often not recognised by those whose intimate familiarity with the equipment being used seems to render them immune to the perils, until, that is, something happens, with all too often fatal results.

One particular afternoon whilst father was on his tea run, which started out like any other afternoon's visit to his gang, the events which followed happened for no apparent reason, and with such suddenness that it is difficult to relate why indeed they happened at all.

After having refreshed the driver and ploughman on the headland nearest the van he was about to set out for the other engine, to give the other driver his bowl of tea. Whether or not he intended, and I suspect not with the can of tea to look after — to travel across the field on the plough, he could never recall, but I expect he intended to cross over the plough rope, behind the plough between it and the engine and then to walk across the unploughed land, whilst he was doing this it happened.

The next he remembered was being on the ground under the tail end of the plough which had started to move back across the field and was beginning to come down into work, the first shear beginning to bite, with the effect that the other shears would follow down in an arc. He was being dragged along by the plough, the shear of the last furrow having got down inside his jacket and waistcoat. The ploughman, or tail end man, whose job it was to ride on the seat at the rear of the plough and hook the rope up on the tail piece of the plough, and also pull the plough down at the beginning of each run, mercifully saw what was happening. He shouted to the driver of the nearby engine, who, as would be the case, was getting his engine ready to move further along the headland for his next pull. The driver immediately realising the situation and reacting swiftly, blew his whistle, once, the signal for the other engine to stop ploughing. By the time that the other engine had heard this whistle and stopped pulling and the flex had gone out of the rope, and the plough had stopped moving, a near miracle had taken place. The tail end man had seized the plough and walked with it holding it up out of the ground, against the natural pull of the earth on the first furrow, and the natural tendency of the plough against the pull of the engine. So

Old Farm, Fairfield, Nr Brookland. My maternal grandparents' home (Mr and Mrs Alfred Apps). His occupation was that of a 'looker' — a contract shepherd in modern parlance, his means of transport being the faithful horse. Old Farm lay across two fields at the end of the small road that passed by the Harvey Farm, my father's home; a distance of a half mile or so.

much so had he kept the shear away from the ground that my father clearly remembers that when the plough stopped moving he literally fell off the plough-share, his clothes having been completely impaled on this. This man had shown not only an alertness to the situation but in those few moments had become possessed with a strength that was almost superhuman.

I feel deeply ashamed to say, that this man's name, to whom my father unquestionably owed his life, is not known to me, and cannot be recorded in this story. For not only should his name have been emblazoned upon the minds of his fellow workmen, but it should have survived on through the generations. This incident, which so clearly could have had the most disastrous of outcomes, was merely dismissed as one of those dangers which faced these men every day of their hard working lives, but which, this time, they had been able to overcome.

Chapter 4

LIGHT ENTERTAINMENT

Hard though the times might have been in the first decade of the century, for rural folk and communities, not every hour was spent at work. Long before television, and even before the wireless, when the mention of cats' whiskers would have conjured up only pictures of the faithful tabby in the minds of the populace there was home made amusement in plenty. As in most villages, where there were larger families, the young of Brookland got together as often as time permitted and made their own fun.

My father and his brothers and sisters, going in gangs with other families, were no exception to this. During their early teens many games were played in the long summer evenings and at the weekends, when they were not at work. Amongst the pranks they got up to, one of the favourite seems to have been changing the gates over on the houses in the street of Brookland under cover of dark. Another was making rafts out of the wooden sheep troughs that were plentiful in the fields by tying a few together and floating them down the rivers or dykes, sometimes falling off and getting wet through in the process or even losing some altogether.

An old army greatcoat button was, so I am told, an excellent plaything. By tying it on a short length of thread and pinning this above someone's window, with the aid of a longer piece of thread attached to it it was possible to hide out of sight of the house and by gently tugging on the thread cause the button to tap on the window pane. It can easily be imagined how frightening this could be to the householder, often, I suspect, knowing children's minds, an elderly one. My father said that eventually the person would come rushing out of the house, alarmed at the incessant eerie tapping, then they would give a quick tug on the thread and the pin would come out and the button could be gathered up, and a hasty if not altogether silent retreat could be made. The householder upon going in again would find to his dismay that the door knob or latch had invariably been given a liberal coating of axle grease or in some cases sheep droppings!!!

It seems no wonder to me that he often recalled the village policeman of the day seemed to be ever on their tails for disturbing the peace of his otherwise tranquil existence.

As they became older their games changed, as could be expected, their growing minds and bodies thirsting for excitement. At this period a favourite game was called 'Jack, Jack strike a light', this being a type of hare and hounds game played in the early autumn as the days shortened and the evenings became darker. One person was chosen from amongst the large group to be Jack and armed with a halfpenny box of matches he would start out. After a short period the gang would call out "Jack, Jack strike a light", where upon Jack would light a match

25

and hold it up for all to see. The flickering light would give a brief indication of where he was, then on he would charge in the dark, the group trying to catch him. Often the group would split up in their efforts or simply became separated in their search around the darkened village. If the evening was still, Jack would sometimes lodge the match in a fence post or similar place and quickly move on. It does not need much imagination to capture the excitement of all this, and the great fun that must have been had by all concerned. Just imagine crossing those plank footbridges in the dark, and fields of slumbering sheep, and think of all the many hazards that could be encountered. On one occasion 'Jack' was known to have stepped over a wall, right through the glass of someone's cucumber frame. One boisterous evening an outside closet got somehow pushed over, much to the consternation of the lady seated inside!!!

A certain parson from a neighbouring parish was, like many of his contemporaries and forbears, a man of thunderous proportions not only in the pulpit, but also in the bar of the local hostelries. He was renowned for his drinking and also for his faithful pony and trap, which could be seen standing for hours at a time well into the night at one or other of the village public houses. He would stagger out in due course and collapse into the trap, whereupon the sagacious pony, knowing the way, would take his master home.

This situation was too good not to escape the eyes of those young men, full of mischief. The old adage surely applies — "The Devil makes work for idle hands". It was not long before the step of the trap was removed one evening whilst the owner was propping up the bar. The step was then replaced but this time reversed and pointing under the trap.

At length the parson came out, watched by many unseen pairs of eyes, and attempted to mount his trap. Picture if you will the scene, as the drunken man endeavoured to find the step of his familiar conveyance, all the while falling about and uttering aloud not very pulpit-worthy comments.

Another version of the same thing was perpetrated on this same gentleman, who really left himself open to the attentions of these pranksters. The docile pony was unhitched from his trap and then reharnessed the wrong way round with his head facing the trap and his tail at the front of the shafts.

The parson, again watched by many from a safe distance, finally collapsed upon the seat of his trap only to find upon giving his steed the command to walk that he went backwards.

On another occasion the same pony was all but unharnessed from the trap and when given the command to walk did just that and stepped straight out of the trap.

With adolescence came other forms of entertainment and amusement, each in their own season. I feel the reader will agree with me that we are all the poorer today for the modern forms of entertainment, for in the days of which I write,

Opposite: John Fowler No. 3197 2nd October 1977 8 NHP KE 6250. — Photo believed to have been taken by Maj. R.J.W. Ind on the same day as the previous picture.
(Copy from the collection of H.J. Clark)

pleasures had to be self made and were all the more rewarding for this, if not to the victims!

The winter evenings brought the village Whist Drives, Socials and Concerts. Many would perform, others, including my mother, would recite monologues and amusing poems, learnt often from a large volume which I possess to this day, 'The Golden Humorous Reciter', others would astound their fellows by their musical virtuosity, most often self taught. My father recalled one family whose four sons would all play a different instrument, their large and seemingly clumsy fingers plucking at strings and racing over keyboards in true professional style. Concert parties would visit from other villages, and from the town of Rye in Sussex just six miles distant over the county boundary.

The mention of Rye brings me to another favourite pastime. This on a Saturday evening at the end of a long week's work would be eagerly looked forward to, a visit to the pictures.

I am told that a large group of young men and women would set off from Brookland on their cycles, the Marsh being so flat that cycles were used by all, to see this newest form of entertainment, the silent movie, and to revel in the antics of Charlie Chaplin and his fellows, or to suffer all the pains and passions of love and intrigue with Mary Pickford and the first film stars, and to do all this to the strains of a hard-worked and untiring lady pounding on the piano.

This entire evening's entertainment would be bought for the sum of six pence at pre-decimal currency (2½ new pence), for the seat at the cinema cost three-pence and a charge of a halfpenny levied by a cycle shop nearby to 'put our bikes up' which left twopence for a fish and chip supper and a halfpenny change.

The leisurely ride back in the late evening was made all the more enjoyable by the happy recounting of the films just seen and the inevitable youthful exuberance, which abounds when the young are together in a large group of friends, some of the boys displaying their apparent skill at riding their bicycles and in many respects showing off to their fellows. I am sure that many a lasting courtship and eventual marriage was formed on occasions such as this.

The summer brought cricket, when work permitted, but my father, starting his steam ploughing duties, was often kept away from this sport of which he was very fond. Brookland, like almost every village, supported a fine cricket team which did well in the inter-village competitions. Teams visited from far and wide and even towns like Rye often went home with their tails between their legs, after suffering a humiliating defeat at the hand of their country-boy adversaries.

The cricket field still flourishes, wedged between the churchyard wall and the main road to Rye and Hastings which bisects the village and within a six-hit from both of the village's hostelries, the Alliance and the George and Dragon. The outfield as always is kept immaculate by the grazing of the flock of local breed sheep, the Romney Marsh, and would do justice to and could well be the envy of many a municipality. Tennis also received its fair share of devotees, my mother being a particularly keen exponent, winning many village trophies to prove her prowess.

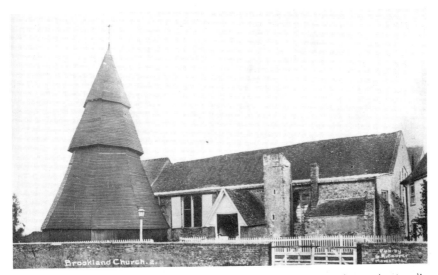

Brookland Church, Romney Marsh, Kent. Dedicated to St Augustine. This predominantly Norman church is one of the 'Cathedrals of the Marsh' — famed for its detached three-tiered belfry, built with beams salvaged from local shipwrecks, as legend has it. The village school's playground abutts the churchyard wall.

The autumn evenings brought darts matches at the locals and bell ringing in the famed shingled campanile of the village church, the only one of its kind known in the country, set apart from the church, built on an octagonal plan rising in layers suggesting the drawing by a child of a Christmas tree. It houses a peal of six bells and is constructed on an oak frame, whose large timbers reputedly had been used before in the construction of sailing ships and men-of-war.

The story of why this steeple was constructed thus has many different versions but the one I prefer is that no bells were originally contained in the old Norman church dedicated to St Augustine. This church sports to this day many unusual features such as a stepped two tier pulpit and uncommonly to this age, fixed family pews.

When it was desired to add bells to the church it was assumed that the weight of a bell tower and its heavy equipment would be too much for the foundations of the already ancient structure, built as it was on marshy ground, and therefore a separate structure was proposed, the present bell tower being the result.

In passing I would add that my late uncle, my mother's eldest brother, did add a large clock to a small tower protruding from the main chancel ramparts for the benefit of the whole village in Coronation year 1952. This was his way of saying thank you to the community, and as an expression of his love for the village which also played a large part in the history of his rise from one of a large family not blessed with wealth to a large land owning sheep farmer.

29

The church, like all churches in a truly rural and close-knit community, where travel, particularly in those days, was out of the reach of most of the people, played a great part in the lives of all the inhabitants. It was essentially a focal point of the village where many occasions of great joy and happiness were enacted, such as christenings and weddings, and also again the not so pleasant but still essential coming together of friends, neighbours and families at funerals and services of remembrance.

The great festivals of the Church's calendar also brought with them the true meaning of pastoral care and a feeling of belonging which essentially was and is today the role of the Church and clergy in our society and never more so than at Harvest Festival, even though this is not an ancient festival of the Christian Church, it only having begun during the middle of the last century at Morvenstowe (Devon). It is then, particularly in a rural community, whose very livelihood stems from the land, that the awe inspiring and frightening reality that they themselves had not alone accomplished a safe sowing and harvest was brought home to them. Probably this realisation was the reason why they were so keen to render gifts of produce and their labours to make sure that their service of thanksgiving was a really splendid occasion.

An eagerly awaited event by many of the villages in the locality was the visit of the travelling circus to the Salts at Rye. This flat piece of land adjacent to the road to the Marsh was the traditional venue of most visiting forms of entertainment. It was originally under the sea and only became dry land when the whole of the Romney Marsh was drained, by the building of sea wall defences and the construction of the military canal and associated dykes.

Great names such as Lord George Sanger and Bostock and Wombwell often made annual appearances on the Salts and were very well supported. This was possibly the heyday of such forms of entertainment, when their only opposition was the newly formed cinema and travelling fairs.

Perhaps the most popular and widely-acclaimed happening took place in the Autumn on November 5th, the Rye bonfire night and Bonfire Boys Parade — a carnival possession which enjoyed a lasting fame that spread over a vast area. People would come from far and wide to see the procession and witness the bonfire.

The bonfire boys were in reality a group or committee of persons dedicated to organising this event. They worked and set out throughout the year to raise finance, organise and construct processional floats and see to the myriad of details that was required to bring this, the largest happening of its kind for miles around, to fruition.

I have been told many times that the decorated floats often included such wonders as fire breathing dragons and ships and the costumes of the participants had to be seen to be believed. There was a torch light procession and the atmosphere that must have prevailed at this spectacle can easily be imagined with sparks flying off the torches held aloft by their bearers to illuminate the floats, as they wended their way through the narrow bunting-festooned cobbled streets streets of that picturesque and ancient town.

The procession would eventually reach its destination on the Salts and the thronging crowd would then possibly get its first sight of the huge bonfire with the inevitable guy. Then would follow the lighting of the fire and the firework display. This alone after the events of the evening, the procession and all the excitement of being there amid the vast crowd would surely have been enough, but much more was at hand to add greatly to the enjoyment of everyone — the travelling fair.

The fair, like the circus in its time, seemed all of a sudden to appear from nowhere and in the space of a few days mushroomed up into a vast gaudily-decorated self-contained village of its own and then all too soon to pack up and disappear, as silently as it had come. It left few traces of its short-lived stay, except perhaps a well trodden patch of grass and a few mounds of rubbish, collected from off the site by themselves, anxious to leave the ground as clean as when they found it, in order to be able to return again another year.

But one thing they did leave behind, which often was to last for a whole life-time, and that was many happy recollections and memories. The travelling fairs of this age brought with them a sense of freedom and a different way of life that was so alien to the persons who flocked to see them.

They set up, often on barren ground, a myriad of items to give pleasure to their patrons and created what seemed like a fairyland of colour and noise, in an age when as we have already seen, the pleasures and experiences open to the rural communities were few, even though those that there were might have been rewarding.

The large heavy loads brought by the fair were soon erected into magnificent, gleaming and ornate castles of pleasure made all the more interesting and alluring by the glow of naptha flares and large arc lights — galloping horses, scenic rides of dragons and whales, swing boats, boxing and wrestling booths, parading shows where the girls out front danced to the music of the can-can, mimicking the age of the naughty nineties, then not so very many years before, side shows of fat ladies, dwarfs and freaks, clairvoyants, strong men, coconut shies and the like, all to add to this feast of pleasure. Over all this was the prevailing curtain of noise, chatter and laughter, the glow of the lights, of many newly electrified lamps and the eerie flickering of the flares. All this and one more and as yet not mentioned facet of the scene — the lingering fingers of smoke which drifted over the whole area, tending to wrap itself around and encompass the very existence of everyone, in a feeling of togetherness.

It was the source of this smoke which drew my father and many of his fellows far more than the delights of the fair itself, for they came to see, admire and wonder at the showman's steam engines.

He recalled, often, his many happy moments, and indeed hours, of standing and watching these great machines, pounding away hour after hour as they generated light for the rides and the whole fair ground. He gazed upon them with the eye of respect of one who, even though he worked daily with such machinery, still held it in awe and admiration.

FOOTNOTE
It must be remembered that not many rides were by that date driven by electricity. The majority were still steam driven, many of the large rides of the day continuing to use steam as a source of power until after the second World War.

Chapter 5

ENGINE DRIVING

The art of steam engine driving in those days was something that was acquired as part of growing up not, as it is today when it is often acquired later in life by people who have had no previous experience with steam.

From his earliest memories my father could always recollect being amongst steam engines and their machinery. His grandfather, as already mentioned, had been in business as a steam ploughing contractor for many years before his birth.

It is natural therefore that, like all growing boys with a healthy and inquisitive mind, he would find himself amidst all that was happening in the farmyard. He told me he could never remember the first time he stood on an engine, indeed he must have been a very young boy at the time of that happening. It is inevitable, therefore, that the knowledge was inherent within him, the phrase often used — being bred in him.

He felt the most real time of learning probably came when, as a cook boy, he used to stand up in the engine with the driver, sometimes his father, and watch and take in the many aspects of this craft. For in many walks of life, and like growing children learning to walk and talk, we in fact learn most by watching and emulating others.

One anecdote he would recall which always stayed clear in his mind took place when he was cook boy with his father's gang and was still only in his early teens. Having been upon the engine with his father and been watched over for a few pulls of the plough, he was obviously thought by the old man then to be ready to have a go on his own. Telling him to keep his water level up, his fire bright, and not to forget to oil up from time to time, he left and rode across the field upon the plough to spend a time in conversation with his fellow engine driver.

My father said he felt so important and was in his element, alone and in charge of a ploughing engine at last. He said he made sure that he did everything that he had been told. Eventually after a considerable time his father returned across the field on the plough, and mounted his engine. Enquiring if all was well my father replied "Yes Father". The old man looked at the water and pressure gauges, then the fire and all seemed well. "Have you oiled up boy?" "Yes Father" Dad replied. In fact he felt sure he had liberally swamped the bearings in oil, just in case.

The old man said no more, but as soon as the plough was running away from his engine, and he had the opportunity he walked along the running board alongside the boiler towards the chimney and put his hand on the crosshead bearing (the connecting rod bearing). He took his hand away smartly and returning to the tender and without saying a word, knocked my father clean to the ground, right out of the engine. Rising to his feet my father enquired what that was for, the reply being "Don't you tell me you have oiled up when you haven't," my father not realising that in those dusty conditions the bearing in question would soon run dry and need attention. In fact he said he never realised it needed doing, or that the old man had referred to that bearing in his instructions.

Nevertheless, Dad said that never again throughout his lifetime with engines did he neglect this bearing. It would seem a rough type of justice in today's society, but goes to show, I feel, not that a lack of love existed between father and son, but rather, what was in those days an accepted form of tuition.

Another incident, similar in many respects to this, happened a few years later, when my father was in his late teens and had been in charge of a complete gang and set of ploughing tackle for a year or two. This particular day they were moving from one job to another and the field to be ploughed was reached by a gateway from a narrow road. It was downhill into the field and the conditions under-foot were not at all good, it being wet and muddy.

My grandfather came on the scene just as Dad was about to enter the field and his offside front wheel struck the gate post. This necessitated reversing up hill and the result was that things became worse rather than better. The old man jumped up in the engine and big as my father was he knocked him off the foot plate again, saying "Get out of the way, and let me have a go." Needless to say he did not do much better and I believe the outcome was that the gatepost was knocked over. A bystander who witnessed the incident, and who knew grandfather, took him to task over this and said "You shouldn't have done that Walt — that boy's a better driver than you are and without doubt the best in the Marsh." At this Dad felt the old man for once in his life was hurt and ashamed at what he had done, for he said he was sorry.

This incident, one of many which happened during those days, illustrates again I feel, not a lack of love or compassion for one's one kith and kin. It is rather, I believe, a small insight into the lives of those hard-worked men, when there was little time for the niceties of life, when the all important task of trying to make ends meet did not leave time or space for reasoned argument. I am sure that, like many other firms in those days, when the country was trying, albeit slowly, to recover from the scourge of the great war, my grandfather was having a job to keep things going. The repair of a simple thing like a gate post was not only an inconvenience, but was also an item of expenditure that could well be done without. Reflecting further on this today; maybe I am being too kind to my grandfather's memory, tiredness and worry may have been partly to blame for his action, which may have explained it — but not excused it, after all it was an unpardonable and self-indulgent act of bad temper and lack of self control and a type of action far too common in its time and in similar situations because the victims, for diverse reasons, were inhibited from retaliation.

Chapter 6

PUMP HOUSES

Since the beginning of time the Romney Marsh, as the name implies, was an area of land of no particular merit, covered for a large part of its surface by the sea.

The situation was to begin to change after the Roman occupation of Britain, for it was the Romans who first set about draining this vast 50,000 acre plain and turning it into some of the most productive and fertile agricultural land in the country. This was achieved by the clever use of drainage ditches and sea wall defences.

The next major step was taken by the Saxons when an enclosing bank – the Rhee Wall – was built from Appledore to Greatstone along the bank of the River Rother to once and for all seal off a vast area of land from the sea and to prevent flooding, protecting the land from the east. It was, therefore, an odd quirk of nature that happened following a great storm of 1287 when the course of the River Rother was diverted taking its present course running out to sea at Rye.

Nevertheless, the battle begun so long before, was continued and gradually the area, a large portion of it up to six feet below sea level, was finally drained. Even to this day, a levy is raised from the inhabitants of the low lying area, which goes towards the cost of maintaining the ditches and dykes. This started as long ago as the twelfth and thirteenth centuries, is known as a 'Scot' and those persons living on higher land, not subject to this levy, are therefore let off 'Scot-free'. Thus it is that a commonly used term of our language owes its origin to this area.

The final major step in this reclamation scheme, and one of its most important, was undoubtedly the digging of the Royal Military Canal. This canal, which runs for 23 miles from Pett Level on the Hastings side of Rye to Hythe, was constructed on the orders of the Prime Minister of the day, William Pitt, in 1804. It was intended as a man-made, easily fortified obstruction, to counter an attack by the French, under the command of Napoleon. This threat, though very real at the time, came to nothing, but the canal was nevertheless completed in four years at a cost of £234,000, and had provided much needed employment for an army of 'navvies' (navigators). It was constructed so as to be at the landward extremity of the Marsh, and right underneath and abutting the higher ground upon its opposite bank. This bank was planted with Elm Trees, and every crossing point was guarded by fortified guardhouses. It was therefore deemed to be easily defended, but alas like so many schemes down through history and even to this present day, it proved worthless. What a different role it might have played if only it had been constructed many centuries before, as all this coastline lay open to the ravages of many marauding troops. Many villages and towns, now well inland, were often sacked and pillaged by invading armies of Norsemen. It was the almost constant warfare with the French which led Edward the Confessor to establish his system of Cinque ports, fortified townships that could raise armed ships to help protect this most open stretch of the country. In return for this service, these ports were granted special privileges.

Useless as the Royal Military Canal turned out to be from a military point of view, its value as a drainage ditch, however, has proved of the utmost importance from the time of its inception, for with this major waterway connected to the sea at each end much of the water from off the land could, by the careful use of the tides, be run off.

Since the earliest of times a body has been set up to watch over and administer the drainage of this area, this in turn being broken down into various regional bodies, whose task it is to look after the floodwater in their sectors. So important is the level of the water within the whole of the Romney Marsh, that the local press carries reports of any meetings of the governing body, and water conditions are reported under the title of 'The Romney Marsh Level'.

In times of severe rainfall and wintry conditions, flooding is liable to occur, and a constant battle is still waged by the authorities to maintain the ditches and dykes. The main weapon of defence and the most beneficial project in this task was the setting up of a series of small independent pumping stations throughout the Marsh area. The person who was responsible for the smooth running of the two major pumphouses in the immediate vicinity of The Harvey Farm, Brookland, the village about which this story revolves, was a much respected member of a farming family, who to the present still farm in that area, Mr Joshua Body. The two pumphouses of particular interest to us are the Breck and the Indraught.

It was during a particularly wet and windy period when flood water covered a great deal of the land around Fairfield Church and The Old Farm, my mother's home, that my father first became acquainted with the Breck pumphouse, an association that started almost by mistake but which was to last for a good many years.

One evening quite late, on a dark and miserable night, a knock came at the Harvey farmhouse door and Mr Body stood there, "Could I have a few words with Walter?" The reason for this urgent visit soon became obvious, as he outlined the predicament that he was in.

The man in charge of the Breck pumphouse had been taken ill and his replacement who knew nothing about engines, had been unable to keep the machinery going. Knowing that Walt had experience with machines as well as having some sons at home and not much work on at that time of the year, he wondered if he could help, if only temporarily?

Before he left that evening Mr Body had been assured that 'young Billy' would be going to the pumphouse first thing in the morning to see what he could do. This was around 1920, my father being in his late teens at that time.

Next morning saw my father armed with a bag of tools and some food trudging

Fairfield Church, Romney Marsh, Kent. Dedicated to St Thomas »a Becket. Fairfield has no village, and the church stands quite alone, some 400 yards from the nearest road. The first church on this site was probably built in the 13th century, and is in all probability the basic structure of the present church, which was encased in brick with the small wooden tower added in the 18th century. Surrounded by sheep most of the year, but often in winter at this time of my narrative by floodwater. The Breck Pumping Station lay in the far distance behind this famous church. Old Farm, Fairfield, my mother's home is the nearest building to this place of worship. Grandmother Apps, despite having a family that eventually was to number eight children, nevertheless found time to look after this church for a good many years.

his way, if not altogether gleefully, across the fields to the Breck, situated as it was over half a mile from the nearest dwelling or farm and reached by a trackway from beyond a farmyard.

The pumphouse, by this time surrounded by floodwater, was a small corrugated building, timber lined on the inside, sitting adjacent to one of the main drainage canals, the only break in the flat and monotonous landscape being the few gnarled willow trees that clung so precariously to the water's edge. The machinery consisted of a large horizontal single cylinder Crossley Oil Engine, with hot-bulb ignition and a six foot diameter flywheel. It was connected to a centrifugal pump, designed to pump 16,000 gallons of water an hour. This pump lifted the water from out of the dykes and pumped it into a drainage canal. This canal, which had been constructed with raised banks, then carried the water out to sea, where by clever handling of the sluices the water was carried away on the ebb tide.

The sight that met Dad's eyes was not encouraging, for it seemed that the temporary man who preceded him had, in his efforts to get things going, partly taken the engine to pieces then left it in this state.

He decided, therefore, to completely dismantle the engine, cleaning it as he went, and then reassemble it afresh. This he did and after making some adjustments, he then cranked the engine over into the firing position, by barring the flywheel round, using the bar against the notched plate on the pumphouse wall. He told me often of the feverish hours he spent doing this, but by late afternoon he was ready to start the engine. At last after a few times the engine fired and settled almost immediately to a steady rhythm. The exhaust noise which, even though muffled, could be heard for a good distance, told him all was well. This steady 'Pompff-pompff' noise which was so soon to become a real part of his every hour was music to his ears, both whilst attending to the engine's needs during the day, and dozing intermittently during the long nights, which stretched ahead, wrapped intimately, so it seemed, in the very warmth that emanated from the engine and bathed in the glow of the solitary oil lamp that cast its swaying shadow over both man and machine.

This first night he recalled sitting down in the old armchair that furnished the pumphouse and eating nearly all his food, not having stopped before in his earnest attempt to get the engine going. He was happy and contented, pleased that his knowledge had been sufficient to overcome the difficulties that had defeated his predecessor and that he had mastered what had been a strange and unknown engine to him.

Next morning he received two visitors, Mr Body and his father who, delighted by the young man's expertise, agreed there and then that he should become the engineman, at least for the foreseeable future.

I am not sure whether or not this prospect at that stage delighted him, but I believe the financial reward of 6d per hour by day and 9d per hour by night was a great inducement to him. For it was on this pay, which when compared with that of the ordinary farm labourer of the day, say 17/- (85p) to 21/- (£1.05) per week, was really quite something, that he saved up to get married.

This first time he stayed on the job for 36 hours and after a night at home he returned for a further 48 hour stretch. This was the pattern that was set for a good number of years to follow. Sometimes even he would work three or four days at a time, when the floodwater was at its worst.

He would know instinctively when the ditches could no longer take the water themselves, and he would invariably be getting ready to leave home long before his father would say, "You had best get out to that pumping station boy." However, his duties made a welcome break from his winter duties on the farm, when no steam contracting took place. These duties most often included looking after the stock and grinding corn and chopping hay for cattle and horses. This played havoc with his asthma, made worse by the dust from the hay and corn husk.

The pumping job helped his finances and was more rewarding than the 10/- he received at home for a full week's work of many hours. Being the boss's son and the eldest of the children he always had to do more than his fair share of the work required, and this seemed the accepted situation in most families.

My mother was a frequent visitor to the lonely pumphouse at the Breck, listening as she walked for the comforting noise of the engine's exhaust — for the most part it was she who used to take his provisions to him. She tells me that a large portion of their courting days were spent there together and that she often took him cowboy books to read, the love of which never left him throughout his life. Father told me that these were happy times for him, even if lonely, and he stated that he got to know every nut, bolt and even knot of wood in that pumphouse over the years. Every detail of this small, but so vital world not only to himself, but the neighbouring farmers, was known to him.

His only other visitor would be, possibly once a fortnight, Mr Body who would call to pass the time of day and ask him for his timesheet. He would also bring with him in his pony cart many of the sundry items that were required for the smooth running of the pumphouse, such as paraffin for the lamp, lubricating oil, cotton waste and so on. He was well pleased with Dad, and even though he never told him to his face, let it be known to his friends, including Grandfather Walter, that Dad was the best man he had ever had at the job.

Mention was made earlier of the other pumphouse in the district, that at the Indraught. I know little about this enginehouse, as my father did not spend as much of his time there, it being much further away from home. The one thing I do know is that this enginehouse contained not an oil engine but a steam engine. This was supplied with steam raised in a vertical flat topped coal fired boiler. This being the case it is reasonable to suppose that the equipment situated at the Indraught was of a much older manufacture than was the case at the Breck. Nevertheless its purpose was the same, to pump water in time of flood.

Had it not been for a quite unusual happening relating to this boiler, possibly I would never have heard of the Indraught at all, and would have had no story to relate. It was during one of his stints as engineer at this pumphouse, and resting from his labours of stoking and so on in the customary arm chair provided that it happened.

Sitting casually watching the changing patterns of light as they danced upon the boiler, caused by the clouds as they raced across the sky, he saw it. What he saw brought all his senses instantly to attention, and then he felt sure that it could not have been, and he must have imagined it, his mind not wishing to accept what he thought his eyes had witnessed. Now fully aware he concentrated all his attention on the boiler, and then he was sure that he had seen it again. What he saw made his hair stand out on the back of his neck, and he would relate until his death of the shock that he had. For he knew he had seen the boiler shell flex, like a man stretching his muscles. It seemed to him that with every beat of the steam engine, the boiler was somehow swelling and contracting.

Convinced now that what he thought he had at first seen, had and was actually happening, he quickly shut down the engine and hastily threw out the fire from the grate. With the dying steam he slowly and carefully topped up the boiler with water to hasten its cooling down. Satisfied that all was now well, he collected his knapsack, locked the door and set off on foot for home.

It was later afternoon when he reached Harvey Farm and luckily for him his father was in the yard. Not expecting to see his son for another day or so, he enquired a little gruffly, "What are you doing home boy? Why aren't you out at the Indraught?" My father's reply was met by the old man with open disbelief "I'm not going back there, the . . . boiler's about to blow up." This his father would not accept and demanded to know the whole story, whereupon he was still not convinced. Finally, in exasperation, my father said "If you don't believe me, you go and steam the . . . thing and see for yourself." And this was what the old man agreed to do, saying that as it was by now teatime they would both go out there in the morning to have a look at it.

Morning found them both at the Indraught where after a summary inspection his father declared that it looked alright to him and a fire was lit. Naturally it took some time for steam to be raised, and this time was taken up with the usual oiling round and maintenance of the steam engine, so essential to ensure the smooth running of the machinery.

Dad told me often that it seemed like ages before they had sufficient steam to start the engine, but eventually all was ready and the pumping commenced, his father convinced by this time that Dad had imagined all that he had related the day before. Nevertheless, he was able to persuade his father to hang on with him for a while as it took a little time for the boiler to really heat up, as it would after many hours of constant use. Dreading that he too had been mistaken, he was in a way relieved when after watching the boiler's every inch of surface so intently that their eyes ached, he finally thought he saw the boiler shell move again. The old man saw it too, and immediately said, "Shut her down boy before the . . . thing blows up."

Again they did as the day before, but this time Dad had help to pack up, and when he finally left the pumphouse that day he took his tools with him, and as he locked the door he vowed never to return to the Indraught again. On their way home they stopped off at Mr Body's where my grandfather had the same difficulty in convincing him that the ancient boiler had become unsafe. Finally, Mr Body agreed, following their pleas and also in view of the still rising flood water to get the 'boiler man' to inspect the suspect piece of equipment. This he did and the news of his visit was eagerly awaited at Harvey Farm. When this duly arrived it was told that on his inspection he had in fact struck the top of the boiler with his hammer and that it had gone right through. My father often wondered how near to death he had been, during those long lonely hours that he attended the boiler, now rendered useless and condemned.

Dad, in fact, never did return to the Indraught and I do not know what was the final outcome of this story, but I suspect that the equipment was replaced with the more modern oil engine pumping system, such as that at the Breck. Even to this day, these two pumphouses exist, now replaced with much smaller constructions housing electric motors and pumps which run automatically, coupled to float switchgear. Similarly, the main pumping station on the Marsh to which all sewers and dykes are drained which is housed just off the main road to Rye is automatically controlled.

The final, as yet, chapter in the battle with the sea over this whole area is played out at this spot. The major factor has been the raising up of the banks containing the River Rother to some considerable height. This allows the water to be pumped from off the Marsh into the river at any time of the day, in times of flood, even when the tide is in, which was not the case before. The water contained within the river is kept isolated from the sea by large hatches which open, again automatically, as the tide recedes allowing the pumped water to escape to the sea. These hatches situated near the mouth of the river at Rye close up once more on the incoming tide. The large pumps used today bear no resemblance to those looked after by my family — being large diameter auger pumps.

The memorial to the crew of the lifeboat *Mary Stanford*.

Chapter 7

RYE FOUNDRY

The ancient cinque port of Rye, as previously stated, lies some six miles or so from the Harvey Farm, Brookland, situated on top of a hill as one approaches from the Marsh to the north-east. One cannot cease to admire the choice of its early inhabitants for the way in which it was developed and fortified, for one can easily see how impregnable its ramparts must have been to an invading army. Sited on top of its hill and, in those days, surrounded by water on three sides, it must have given a great sense of security to its townspeople as they scanned the horizon for any sign of invasion, looking almost invariably across the channel.

The main road from Ashford to Hastings now travels across the flat marsh area, bisecting Brookland as it does so. It skirts the narrow cobbled streets of Rye by a circuitous route around the base of the knoll on which the town stands. This road passes the front gables and doorways of an old established firm of engineers known in its time to many generations as either The Rother Iron Works or else The Rye Foundry.

The foundry buildings as mentioned fronted by the road, border that area known as the Salts and back onto the River Rother, where still many fishing boats have their home port, branded with the prefix RX. It is the waters of the Rother that lead them through the picturesque Rye Harbour hamlet situated some mile and a half from the town itself to the risky water of the English channel and the fickle tides of Camber Bay. It is off this shoreline that a tragic accident befell the crew of the Rye lifeboat in 1928 when seventeen brave souls from this tiny community perished. A memorial to them stands at the minute churchyard of Rye Harbour church, the inscription upon which reads 'To the memory of the seventeen brave men, the crew of the *Mary Stanford* lifeboat, who perished in a heavy gale while gallantly responding to the call for help from the s.s. *Alice of Riga* on the morning of 15th November, 1928'.

One can only stand in abject admiration and great humility in the face and presence of men, such as these, who go down to the sea to rescue others in distress, when conditions are such that they knowingly risk their own lives.

This tragedy, which robbed this tiny hamlet of its greatest sailors and much of its youth, must surely rank as being amongst the greatest acts of heroism rendered by any small community. For amongst those who lost their lives on this terrible night, no less than three families lost three of each of their own, in one case, a father and two sons, with two other families losing two each of their number.

The awful truth about this dreadful night being that this hand-rowed lifeboat's valiant attempt at a rescue was really in vain, as the s.s. *Alice* was given assistance by another vessel.

41

Noticing on my last visit that in one case, mercifully *only* one person was lost from a particular family, that of Charles Southernden at the age of 22 and saying a silent prayer for this, sharp focus was brought to my mind on leaving the churchyard. Passing through the tiny lychgate of the church of the Holy Spirit, my eye caught the list of those from this hamlet who lost their lives during The Great War. Of this one family no less than nine other persons bearing the same name had given of their lives in the services of their King and country. And now of the remaining family one more was to give the supreme sacrifice in an effort to help others.

With tears welling up in my eyes, I felt immense pride in being one of a nation, that could raise families like those of that tiny hamlet. What kind of special persons are they that can go on and on giving of this rare quality of heroism and bravery, who by their very deeds bring a new meaning and sense of awe to Great Britain? We are surely a privileged race to count such as those within our number.

Returning to Rye Foundry, even situated as it is in the neighbouring county of Sussex, to those staunch men of Kent; it was to this firm that the Newton family turned for all its heavy repair jobs that could not be carried out by themselves in the workshop and forge at Harvey Farm.

All the ploughing engines owned and operated by the family firm were single cylinder Fowler engines. They came into the family's ownership in a variety of ways often having had more than one owner previously. By the period of which I am writing, the first and second decades of this century, these engines were of considerable age. Two of the pairs of engines according to their builders, John Fowler of Leeds, were, in fact, manufactured as long ago as 1870 and numbered respectively 1199/1200 and 1437/38. It was, therefore, not surprising that by 1920 these engines should be in need of more than minor attention. In fact new boilers were required by that date. It is I feel a measure of the skill of manufacture, and a compliment to their builders, that this kind of major repair and replacement should not have been deemed necessary until a hard working life of nearly half a century should have been accomplished. It must not be overlooked that working so near to the sea, as was often the case with the family's engines, and using whatever water sources were available might be expected to have had an extremely adverse effect upon the metal, and yet they gave good service for all this time, probably because the boiler plates were of wrought iron.

This was not, however, the case with the boiler tubes and firebox stays, as my father recalled many times having to go out to effect on-the-spot repairs when breakdowns occurred. Often he would accompany the blacksmith Dave Cottington or sometimes even his father. In the early days their trips would have been made by pony and trap well loaded down with the necessary tools and so forth, but later, with the advent of the motor car, about which more will be written later, the journeys were more comfortable. Dad recalled working late into the night replacing boiler tubes and the odd stay. It was his lot, being younger, to be the one who would have to work inside a hot engine firebox, with the aid of an oil lamp. Imagine the scene — in the corner of some strange field, or along the headland where the engine had just finished a day's work. Firstly they would have to remove the ashpan and still-hot firebars from the engine, the fire having been thrown out by the driver at the end of work. After inspecting the failed or suspect piece of equipment to ascertain what was required in the form of a repair, the water in the engine would then have to be drained down to a level which would allow the repair to be carried out. This water, which was as often as not near boiling, then reduced the area under the engine to a quagmire, in which they had to work.

After the boiler tube or stay had been replaced, the firebars and ashpan had to be replaced, and the engine topped up with water, either from the horse-drawn water cart left by the farm's carter at the end of the day for this purpose, or else from the nearest ditch, using a bucket. The fire would then be lit and, after its being ascertained all was well, it would be banked up again and left in readiness for the regular driver, who during all this hasty activity was trying, albeit I suspect without much success, to snatch a few hours sleep in the van parked nearby.

To return to the role played by the Rye Foundry in the family's fortunes, when an engine had to be reboilered it would be driven to the foundry in the autumn or early new year for the work to be carried out.

It was at this time that my father would be sent to live in Rye, where he lodged with his Aunt Miriam, the wife of his Uncle Arch, who ran a small forge and blacksmith's shop known as the Tower Forge. This lies immediately under and abutts onto the Landgate tower, one of the original fortified towers of the ancient town built in 1329 when Edward III made grants for further fortifying the town. Dad was then employed by the foundry to work on the engine in question. I believe he was taken on during these times in some form of apprenticeship, and I suspect that this was done with a view to making the family's bill for the job correspondingly smaller, though it was also a way of helping the foundry over the problem of lack of manpower, suffered by many similar firms as a result of the Great War which had not long been over. Dad recalled his father being very friendly with the foundry's owner and also that his bill for lodgings was settled by the latter. During his many months at the foundry my father learned a great deal of his engineering skills, which he was to put to good use during the rest of his life. He remembered, with a mixture of affection and at the same time awe and that reverence that Tom Brown might have had for his schoolmaster, the general foreman of the establishment, Bill West. He was one of the old school, as it were, a devout and strong character, who ruled over the foundry and its workshop with a rod of iron. Dad said that one word from him was enough, for he was a strict disciplinarian, but it is a measure of the soundness of his teaching that his methods and skill were passed on to his young apprentices, never to be forgotten during their lifetimes. Bill West was a good few years later to establish his own firm known as West's Engineering Co. at Camber.

Under his direction the engine in for reboilering would be completely stripped down and anything that required attention such as new bearings and piston rings would be attended to whilst it was at the works.

The new boiler would have by this time arrived by rail, having already been ordered from the Oxford Steam Plough Co. Records exist elsewhere of these complete boilers being delivered for £164, so it is probable that those delivered to Rye cost about the same sum. The fitting of the cylinder and motion work to this new boiler was a job that required the utmost skill, in order to marry it to the old cylinder casting and ensuring that both parts fitted exactly, so as to be steam tight.

Dad recalled often that Bill West would do all the marking out of the new boiler himself, not trusting anyone else with this skilful task. He said that the experienced man, with the simplest of tools, a measure, straight edge, plumb-bob, piece of chalk and a handful of other oddments would clamber about the engine and boiler chalking here and there. Finally, when satisfied by eye as well as by measurement that all was well, he would instruct his men, who had watched him perform his task with feelings ranging from awe to disbelief, to carry on and work to his guidelines, all the while watching over them intently, as a hen with a young brood of chicks. My father told of the many hours he spent with a scraper and file, trying time and again using red lead as a marking paste, to shape and fit the cylinder casting to the new boiler barrel. He said he would file away, and keep lowering and raising the casting, for what seemed like hundreds of times, until Bill West said at last that he was satisfied with the joint and that he would be confident that it would be steam tight.

Another job Dad hated, which he would often be called upon to do, would be to get inside the tender, by going through the manhole, and chipping away the scale that had formed there, in order that the inside could be painted. He said that not only did he hate the confined space, but that the heat and dust used to play havoc with his chest and asthma. Nevertheless, he recalled, if Bill West said do it, you did it.

Finally, after many weeks, the engine would be ready to return to the Harvey Farm and most often Dad would drive it away from the foundry, down into the Marsh, ready to return to what was thought to be many more years of service, but was in reality to be only a decade or so.

This was the pattern that must have been set for quite a number of years for records show that many of the family's engines received the same treatment. Even as late as 30th November 1944 three of the engines found lying idle at the farm on that date had the familiar Oxford pattern safety valves fitted, together with a plate fastened to the smokebox door reading Oxford S.P. Co.

It is, to my mind, a very sad fact that none of these engines, with their early date of manufacture and subsequent re-building by the foundry, survive. They would be unique today.

At least one other engine was reboiled at Clark's Engineering Works at Elwick Iron Works, Elwick Road, Ashford. The late John Russell recorded on 30th March 1945 'Newton was one of the last to have an engine reboiled. Clark rebuilt one with an Allen boiler, I saw them fetching it from the shop, I think about 1920.' It is interesting to note that my father's youngest sister, Sybil, later married Reg Ward, who as a young man had been an apprentice at Clark's works. Later on he was to serve as a representative for George Thurlow & Son Ltd of Stowmarket, Suffolk, general agricultural engineers. This firm supplied parts and stores for steam engines, and it was whilst doing this that he regularly called upon Grandfather, where he met his future wife.

Ruston Proctor 8 NHP T.E. No. 32404 1907. — Photo taken by G. Eastes on 9th September 1951. (Copy courtesy of B.D. Stoyel)

Chapter 8

LIGHT RELIEF

During the long hours worked by steam plough men which have been documented by many other writers almost to the point of legend, incidents happened from time to time that broke the tedium that otherwise filled their days.

Amongst those that my father recalled, the following stand out in my memory. The first is the time the plough gang were working in the early autumn at the farm of a regular client. This farmer, as many of his contemporaries, made his own cider, the fame of which was well known to all those who visited the farm. This particular year must have been a vintage one as the autumn days were fine and sunny. The farmer, as usual, had given them a gallon jar of cider and had said that, as they were near the farmyard and knew where the cider was kept, should they need any more, then the cook boy could re-fill the jar.

On the Friday afternoon it seems the crew took the farmer's words too literally and the cook boy was seen to visit the cider store more than once. The result was inevitable, and Father recalled that by tea-time they had to stop ploughing — unheard of in their circle — especially for piece-work men. Having stopped for the night, they decided that a few more swigs from the jar might help their sleep — which came no doubt swiftly, if not peacefully, and liberally interrupted all night long by first one and then the other of the men having to pay a visit to the great outdoors.

Next morning, Saturday, dawned to a hard start, for the engines had not been banked down sufficiently to cover the unusually long night and the fires were out. Finally, a start to the operations was made, but try as they might, they could not seem to get the hang of it, or rather, away from the hangover. Dad stated that as foreman of the gang he decided to call it off for the weekend at about mid-morning. Returning home early he was left in no two minds about the effects of the Demon Drink after explaining their predicament to his father.

It might seem that his father's words fell on ears that were deaf, as another incident relates, but I suspect that a fair amount of time had elapsed between the two incidents.

Finishing work at one farm after a particularly long stint, and moving the tackle from off the higher land down onto the Romney Marsh to the farm of their next customer, they found that their path led through the village of Stone-in-Oxney. It was their intention to stop at the friendly Crown public house just long enough to quench their thirsts and then to move on to the next farm so as to try to set up before dark, ready for an early start next morning. As luck would have it, or not, according to one's point of view, some of my father's mates — fellows with whom he played cricket in summer when work permitted, and darts in the winter — were also enjoying a quiet pint in the Crown. These contemporaries of his did not work the long hours that the ploughmen did, nor did they enjoy the financial rewards that came with their hard labours. It has been stated many times that the ploughmen were looked upon with a sense of awe by their fellowmen of the day, for their somewhat nomadic existence, in charge of their mighty steeds and with money, albeit little by today's standards, in their pockets was a lot not enjoyed by the casual farm labourer. This, then, often led to a sense of detachment, but a no less friendly atmosphere existed between them.

On this particular day — late in the summer, they arrived just as the hostelry opened its doors for the evening, and one pint and friendly rivalry on the dartboard led to another and so on, all the while thinking that time was slipping by only slowly, which was not the case, for by the time they came to leave it was almost dusk. The village of Stone lies on the Isle of Oxney, and as the title states this is truly an island, one of several that in this part before the drainage of the Marsh was at one time surrounded by tidal water. To this day one has to cross a bridge in any direction to gain entrance to or exit from the village. Therefore, to reach the Marsh on this particular evening their normal path would have been to travel on to Appledore on the more level road and turn right into the Street, down over the Military Canal via the main road bridge. This journey, some five miles or thereabouts in distance, would have meant their leaving the Isle of Oxney by the toll bridge at the Ferry Boat Inn.

Whether or not it was the prospect of this longer journey, or else the impending toll charge, or their beer-depleted pockets that made them change their minds, I do not know. But what I do know, however, is that they chose to go in the other direction, forking to the right at the Crown.

Mention ought to be made here of the toll bridge at the Ferry Boat Inn. There had been a toll levied at this point from early times. The wooden bridge was done away with in favour of a brick construction over the Burmarsh dyke in the late eighteenth century, but nevertheless, tolls were still enforced until the 1930s and a board affixed to the wall of the Ferry Boat Inn shows the charges that were in force at the time of the lifting of tolls in September 1933. It can be seen from these charges that an entire steam ploughing outfit would have been the subject of a considerable levy, bearing in mind the wages of the day.

The 'Street' at Appledore also mentioned above deserves further comment. This grand sounding name applies to the main wide thoroughfare through the village, flanked on either side by some interesting houses, many of which date back to the fifteenth century and have witnessed many scenes down through the years. Affixed to the wall of the mediaeval church, a board proclaims that the village had had mixed fortunes. 'The sea creeks on which Appledore once stood brought invaders as well as the trade which made it prosper. Danish Vikings made their base there and were only dislodged by King Alfred after five years fighting. In 1380 the French sailed in and burnt the village.'

47

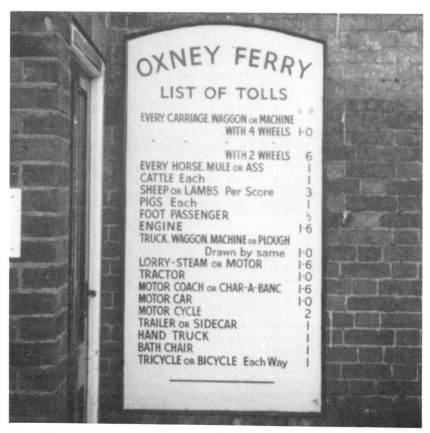

OXNEY FERRY

LIST OF TOLLS

	s	d
EVERY CARRIAGE. WAGGON or MACHINE WITH 4 WHEELS	1	0
" " " WITH 2 WHEELS		6
EVERY HORSE. MULE or ASS		1
CATTLE Each		1
SHEEP or LAMBS Per Score		3
PIGS Each		1
FOOT PASSENGER		½
ENGINE	1	6
TRUCK. WAGGON. MACHINE or PLOUGH Drawn by same	1	0
LORRY-STEAM or MOTOR	1	6
TRACTOR	1	0
MOTOR COACH or CHAR-A-BANC	1	6
MOTOR CAR	1	0
MOTOR CYCLE		2
TRAILER or SIDECAR		1
HAND TRUCK		1
BATH CHAIR		1
TRICYCLE or BICYCLE Each Way		1

The Oxney Ferry list of tolls in force at the time of their abolition in 1932 on 'The Ferry Boat Inn' wall, Isle of Oxney.

'Men from Appledore joined the great peasants revolt in 1381 when one of the major buildings known as Hornes Place was sacked by Watt Tyler's men. Jack Cade's army also marched through the village in 1450.'

I am told also that great pageantry was seen in the Street in the middle ages. The Royal Court used to arrive in the village from London and take to sailing barges, in which they travelled to Rye, there embarking into larger craft to sail to France, all this, of course, before the Military Canal played its final part in the reclamation of the area.

We must, however, return to our story. Leaving the warmth of the public house to friendly cat-calls and much waving of arms and tankards by their friends, and aware now only too well of the fast approaching darkness, the ploughing gang set off. Fortified by 'Dutch courage' they assured one another that the stories they had heard about the wooden bridge on that road not being strong enough to hold the weight of a ploughing engine just could not be true.

One thing was sure, however, and that was that the die has been cast, because once they set out down that road there was no way that they could turn round or go back, the road being too narrow. My father, as foreman of his gang, was driving the first engine towing the plough. The second engine hauling the living van, cultivator and water cart followed closely behind. This was the usual formation adopted by steam plough gangs on the road.

The gearing on that old 8hp engine must have rung out clear on the night air, and the wheels crunched on the stones as they made their way along. Even to this day the road is very narrow. It skirts the village, passing close by the church, shaded by satanic looking yew trees, rising all the while as it follows the contours of the hill until suddenly it breaks out near the top of Stone Cliff. Turning left the road drops sharply away and notices posted either side proclaim that the gradient drops at 1 in 8, and that the road is narrow with only passing places. Surely this is another of those roads, all too familiar in the most rural areas, which must originally have been cut by a drunken man leading a horse, bounded by high banks and trees and twisting and turning through many right-angled bends.

Picture that ploughing gang — now in darkness broken by the glow from their fireboxes, and the occasional spark from their chimneys. Mercifully none but the brave or stupid would have been abroad in that same road that evening. The last corner safely behind the road drops steadily away. In front lies the Military Canal — at our feet — whilst stretching away to the sea out of sight in the distance beyond Rye lies the vast flat plain of the Romney Marsh.

As the plough gang descended the hill that evening, their thoughts became sharply focused, as their heads cleared, on the task and danger that lay ahead, namely the prospect of having to cross that painfully inadequate bridge, now imminent. Dad often remarked how clear was the memory of that moment as he gingerly nosed his old engine up onto the bridge — "It was as if it was only yesterday" he would say — amazing how fear clears the head! He told how he distinctly felt the bridge sag as it bore the full weight of the engine and how he had to literally 'open her up' to climb up out of the bridge as it were.

Safely on the other side, he watched as the other engine followed suit, and recalled peering through the gloom to catch the look on the other driver's face, which had to be seen to be believed! The hair on the back of his own neck was standing up for quite a while as he remembered thinking of what the consequences might have been if the bridge had collapsed. Needless to say, this was an exercise that was not repeated, and not much was said about it at the time for fear the news travelled back to Harvey Farm. Moderation in his drinking habits from then on was surely a result of incidents such as these.

This bridge was finally demolished by the military at the commencement of the Second World War. Sappers blew it up in common with many other bridges over the Royal Military Canal, leaving only a few at major crossing points which were heavily defended and fortified. After the war it was replaced with a steel bridge, still with wooden handrails, which is still in use.

The county of Kent in those years about which I am writing had an enormous influx of visitors each summer, but not the tourists of latter years. They came to work in the fields, as seasonal workers at all manner of tasks, such as fruit picking, potato picking, hoeing and in fact anything that was required of them during the changing seasons. The annual influx of Londoners for the hop picking was a spectacle in itself and is widely known.

Gipsies, or Pykies, to give them their Kentish title, fell into a different category however, because unlike the other visitors they did not return to other homes at the end of the season but stayed on living in their caravans on any piece of waste ground, and scratching a living by all manner of means. What I now relate must have happened during mid-summer because the ditches at that particular place were dry.

The ploughing gang were working in the field and my father's engine ran along a headland bordered by a dry ditch. When night-time came the cessation of the day's activities found his engine opposite a small triangle of ground on the other side of the ditch, on which a small group of gipsies was encamped.

Leaving the engine, as usual, all banked up for the night he retired to the house van with his gang. On returning at first light to rustle up the fire in readiness for the day's work he found he had no coal in the tender with which to do this. He stated that it had been picked clean, even though it had been filled by the farmer's carter not long before knocking off time the previous day.

As the darkness of night gave way reluctantly to the light of day, all was revealed. For there for all to see was a pathway clearly marked out by black coal dust from the side of his engine, down across the ditch, up the other side to the gipsies' camp.

Deeds such as this required drastic action and he roused the sleeping occupants of the caravan by banging on it with a stick. The sound of muttering and swearing from within was not at all gentlemanly and he would smile when recounting this tale.

When at last a head poked out of the door he enquired of its owner, "What have you done with my coal?" Whereupon the sleepy but irate occupant said, "Coal, Mister, what coal? We haven't seen any coal."

Father said that after a few more exchanges, none very good natured or polite, when it became obvious that he was getting nowhere, he left upon issuing a final ultimatum, this being that if the coal had not been returned to the engine by the time he had had his breakfast then he would fetch the other engine over from the other side of the field and pull the caravan over that . . . ditch with the rope.

He remembered that, as if by magic, the coal returned to the tender, and work was resumed, if a little later than usual, a wary and untrusting eye being kept on one another from both sides of the ditch throughout the day.

Chapter 9

ACCIDENTS

As mentioned in previous pages many incidents were to occur which left their mark on those persons concerned. As anyone who had worked long hours with heavy machinery would doubtless know, other events would be bound to happen which would leave even greater scars on its participants and would thus surely come under a classification of their own — accidents.

Familiarity, says the cliché, breeds contempt, and I feel justifiably so, as inevitably the constant use of materials and machinery leads to a false sense of security and an almost blind imperception of the inherent dangers therein. An accident occurred in 1939, which was to leave a permanent scar on my father and a lasting if not visible mark upon my grandfather.

This happened in a field known as Saddlers Wall field, Brookland, no more than three-quarters of a mile away from the Harvey Farm. It was in this same field that another incident took place some years later, and I believe I am right in saying that this was the last field in which the family carried out steam plough-ing. How often in life, the same places or same events keep cropping up, when by all the law of averages the result should have been so different.

On this occasion the threshing gang, with Grandfather in charge, had either just arrived at the field or were just setting up to thresh another stack. The engine in use was the elderly Aveling and Porter and the threshing machine a Marshall, the usual gang consisting of land girls and Bert Huggett being present.

Anyone who had worked with such machinery would know that it is essential that the threshing machine be placed so as to be level. This is to ensure that the threshing process can be performed correctly, and that the corn and straw can be evenly placed over the sieves and that the machinery is not unevenly loaded thus rendering it inefficient. All threshing machines are equipped with spirit levels built into their frames for this purpose.

The engine also had to be placed fairly level to ensure that the long driving belt ran true and stayed firmly on the flywheel and driven pulley. These had slightly convex surfaces to further improve on this, as all running belts will rise to the highest point on the surface of the wheels to which they are attached. It does not require much imagination to realise that in virtually every site visited by the threshing gang this prerequisite of a level site was not available even in a flat area like the Marsh. Picture if you will the average stackyard in mid-winter, cramped, muddy and full of cart tracks, often frozen solid or else flooded to ankle depth and imagine trying to find a level spot.

Therefore the levelling process was achieved by the use of one of two methods or a mixture of both, as conditions dictated, namely either to dig a hole under some wheels or else to jack up the wheel and place baulks of timber under them.

Such was the scene that presented itself to my family on that fateful day in 1939. The gang had just finished one stack and prepared to set up the machine in readiness to thresh the next one in the row. All was going well, a well-tried process was being adopted that had been carried out umpteen times without mishap.

What followed was to change all this irrevocably. Grandfather was holding one wedge of timber to be driven in to firm up the wheel on the threshing machine in order to stop it creeping forward off its blocks as the engine took up the strain on the driving belt. The sledge-hammer swung down repeatedly and all of a sudden it caught the wedge on its side and shot off and struck Grandfather a glancing blow on the side of his head. The unhappy man wielding the hammer was sure as were all the rest of the gang that the blow that felled the governor had indeed killed him. He was rushed from the site as fast as the transport of the day would allow to Ashford District Hospital, where I am happy to relate that he came round in due course and had suffered no worse than a fractured skull!! This necessitated a prolonged stay in hospital for observation. Knowing my grandfather as I did I cannot think that he would have made a very serene incumbent of any hospital bed.

My father had at this time been married some fourteen years and in an effort to improve his situation in life he had left the farm and moved away to a neighbouring village. He and my mother had set up home at Rose Cottage in the parish of Snargate, in a typical house for that part of Kent, being double-fronted with weather board to the upper part of its structure. This small holding had been rented for them by Grandmother who, being concerned that they had no home of their own following their marriage, decided to help. They had for the first two years of their lives together lived at the Old Farm, Brookland, my mother's home. The attraction of this place though was the small paddocks and orchard that went with the cottage. It was here where they lived for thirteen years that my father kept some sheep of his own and ran a small holding. It was during these years together that they were sublimely happy, and much visited and envied by their respective brothers and sisters. To supplement his income my father worked as gardener/chauffeur — both jobs he hated — to an elderly gentleman of the village — a Mr Clarke — a stockbroker by trade. I am not sure whether he ever worked regularly, if only on a casual basis for his father at this time, or whether or not with the decline in the family's contracting business he had broken all ties with the firm. What I do know, however, is that on this occasion they sent for him with all haste, to help them out of the predicament that they found themselves in. For his brothers, one away at the war, another with his own business to run, were all occupied in some way or another and presumably not able to help. It was recognised by all, however, that none of them had the same bent for steam as my father, and neither did they show his enthusiasm for it.

Having been made aware of the situation that existed he decided that he would drive the engine for them and that a start would be made on the morrow. This was done and all went well until a break was made for lunch.

Before starting again for the afternoon, the first job was always to oil round, one of the gang seeing to the threshing machine, my father attending to the engine.

He always told me that someone had been on the engine during their lunch break, for what purpose I cannot say, but whether or not this was the case it would be impossible to prove. Yet the engine was the recognised place to go for a smoke, pipe or cigarette, the manstand of which being the only place in the rickyard deemed safe for this purpose. The ever present danger of fire was always in the minds of those engaged in threshing. But during the oiling process for some reason, and I know not how, except that I suspect the reversing lever could not have been in the central position which would have prevented the linkage from moving, the crankshaft revolved. Whether or not it was due to a person pulling on the belt or whether it was my father's lack of familiarity with this engine, for it must be remembered that this was Grandfather's usual mount, no one has been able to decide. But turn over the crankshaft did just at the moment my father was oiling the motionwork with the result that the crankpin of the main bearing caught the thumb on his left hand and tore it off. He remembered holding his hand up and shouting "Look at my b . . . . . thumb", which was hanging by a thread of skin.

Fortunately for him one of the farmer's men present had some previous knowledge of first-aid, having served in the Great War, and he quickly came to Dad's aid and covered up his hand applying a tourniquet to his wrist to stem the flow of blood. He now was rushed to Ashford District Hospital where he underwent an emergency operation to tidy up the stump that was left of his thumb, and when he came round, would you believe, he was but two beds away from his father in the same ward.

I can remember very clearly, even though I was but two and a bit years old at the time, being taken to visit my father in hospital. We, my brother and I, were not allowed into the ward, but I can recall standing next to him and seeing my father walk up towards us smiling and trying to converse with us through the large glass partition. I cannot, however, recall seeing my grandfather at this time, who undoubtedly was now doubly concerned about the lack of a driver to attend to their unfinished work.

Trugs Huggett told me at a later date that soon after Grandfather had returned home, when he was supposed to be resting, he said one day, "Trugs, you had better go and light that old Aveling and I'll be away later to finish the job." This he did, and the remainder of the stack was finally threshed.

THE OLD FORGE, BROOKLAND

Chapter 10

EMPLOYEES

Besides the immediate members of the family, all of whom, when available — girls as well as boys — would be pressed into helping to staff the family concern, there were others who deserve mention, namely the employees who, by their length of service and loyalty, attained a category of their own. I am sure that in every industry and small family business there are these faithful people similar to those about to be mentioned, who carve out for themselves a niche in the hearts of the family they serve and play a valuable part in the overall fortunes of their employers.

Such a person was Dave Cottington the blacksmith. He has already been briefly mentioned in earlier pages, but rightfully should command more than a few lines of type. Dave was, I believe, born in Brookland, and upon leaving school went to work at the village forge, which incidentally is still used by a working blacksmith. No sooner had he started there than the owner, his tutor, was taken ill and I am told he virtually taught himself the trade. I suspect it was the feeling of wanderlust that would have been present in him that made him join the army when still a young lad. This led to basic training at Aldershot in the Royal Engineers. Soon he found himself shipped to South Africa to play his part in the Boer War. Events there coloured his life and left memories that he was often to recall later on in life.

It was inevitable with his skill as a blacksmith that he should become a military farrier, when it is remembered the army employed many horses and mules to support infantry besides the cavalry regiments. Unfortunately, he became one of thousands who were imprisoned in the seige of Ladysmith.

Years later when he worked in the forge at the Harvey Farm, my father would often remark to him as young boys are often wont to do, "I'm starving," to which Dave used to reply, "You don't know what starving is my boy." He related how, during the seige, all the horses and other animals were killed and eaten, even rodents going the same way. Army boots were boiled in an attempt to make them supple in order that the leather could be chewed. Thus it was that Dave spoke with authority on the subject of being hungry. He also visited Mafeking after the seige of that city had been lifted. Returning to his native village soon after the war, he took the post of blacksmith to the family and it was an association that was to flourish for a good number of years.

Following the death of my great grandfather in 1917, and the move of his son from the cottage into the farmhouse, Dave took up residence in Elm Cottage.

Opposite: Dave Cottington — The Family's Blacksmith — returned to the village forge when steam ceased at 'The Harvey' — shown here as an elderly gentleman (on the left) with some of his contemporaries.

'Man and Boy'. Grandfather Walter (on engine) with his ever faithful employee and friend
Trugs Huggett.

This was more convenient for him, as he was now situated in sight of his forge. He remained with the family until all steam ploughing finished and, apart from the steam threshing, the business as he had known it had ceased.

After this he returned to the village forge, living not in the forge house but in a new council house. Here he finished out his time, a true man of the village, who had served not only my family, but also the community in which he lived, in full measure.

The second person to fall into this special category is one whom I met for the first time early in 1981, in his seventy-first year, although he is a person about whom I had heard much, his name cropping up in any conversation dealing with the firm. As a young schoolboy, he tells me, he could not wait to get out of school and rush down to the Harvey Farm and be amongst the engines. His holidays also were spent there, helping, as best he could, in all manner of tasks asked of him. His enthusiasm, I am sure, did not limit him, even if his tender years and lack of strength might have from time to time. The old adage of one volunteer being worth ten pressed men surely applied to him. It was inevitable therefore that he should seek his employment with the family upon leaving school. His loyalty was such that he was only to leave their employ when finally the farm was sold long after all the steam engines and equipment had been disposed of. His name is Bert Huggett but he is affectionately and for some inexplicable reason known to all as 'Trugs Huggett'. His main role was played during the latter years of the firm, especially during the wartime threshing era. He was one of the mainstays of the threshing gang and was known as an exceptional feeder of the drum. He most often steered the engine for Grandfather when moving from farm to farm and can also recount many episodes, some amusing, others frightening, that occurred during the years.

His affinity to and fondness for his employer — my grandfather Walter — was such that it went far beyond that of friendship. This was clearly illustrated to me, at that first meeting, when I showed him a photograph of his long since employer driving a traction engine. This old countryman looked at it and was immediately moved nearly to tears. With a voice full of emotion, he said in his stammering way "Poor old Walter — I loved that old man — he was my old friend he was — he was a good old engine man — I would love to have a photo like that — If I had a photo like that it would make my day." When one considers what they had been through together — all the work that they had accomplished in good times and in very bad times, and that it was twenty years after the death of his old friend, his words were a moving insight into the meaning of loyalty and friendship. His enthusiasm for steam still lives on to the extent that in his garden shed he has a small steam engine and scale model threshing machine that he has built himself.

Reuben Barham, however, was of a different generation and one of the old school. Apart from members of my own family, he was one of the main ploughing engine drivers. He came to the Harvey Farm soon after the family set up business there and continued in their employ for a good number of years. He was a skilled engine man, not easily ruffled, who in his steady methodical way was able to cope with virtually any situation that presented itself. I am told that he had a real feeling and affinity for the steam ploughing engine. He served his time with my great grandfather and my grandfather and indeed my father would often recall him in the many conversations we held about days of long ago.

Yet the surprising thing about Reuben and his work on the Marsh is the fact that during all this time his home was in Rye. He lived in a small house built sideways to, and almost on, the main road at 20 South Undercliff. The tiny house, overshadowed by the steep cliff rising almost perpendicularly from against its far wall, is within sight of and some two hundred yards away from the Rye Foundry.

Reuben never rode a bicycle, but would walk the six miles to the Harvey Farm every weekday. If the engines were away from the farm at work then like the rest of the crews he would walk to them on the Monday morning, arriving in time to start and live for the week in the van.

When ploughing ceased at the Harvey Farm Reuben retired and, according to a gentleman whom I met recently, it would seem he finished out his time doing casual work at the foundry. "Even as an old man — big and strong, who must have been about 80 — he would still lift up two three-quarter hundredweight casting blocks and stagger along with them."

Chapter 11

THE CAR

As is invariably the case, war-time brings with it not only bloodshed, bereavement and hardship, but also paradoxically a measure of prosperity. This had always been the case with many communities, not the least of these the agriculturists.

The drive for home grown food production during the Great War resulted in my family being given full employment and consequently a certain measure of affluence. Whilst there were never any halcyon days in their struggle to make ends meet and raise their growing family, my grandparents were sufficiently well off at the end of the war to consider other modes of transport than the pony and trap. They bought a car — the first one to arrive in the village of Brookland — a Ford Model T, a 'tin lizzy', The pony was presumably sold off and the trap and one or two other assorted carts, governess, gig and so on were stored in the cart shed, where I can remember seeing them and indeed playing on them many years later.

It would seem with this new-found form of transport that my forebears took on a new lease of life, and even sampled the delight of the occasional social outing, no doubt much to the envy of their contemporaries.

This shiny new vehicle blessed with the most modern of inventions, electric lights, as well as the old standby acetylene lamps, sported a drop-down hood and wooden spoked wheels and came in a neat shade of black.

Grandfather now, possibly for the first time in his life — for he was a hard working man and not one led to boast — decided to indulge in one of the social graces, that of taking tea with his friend — some five miles away from home. He duly set off this Sunday afternoon driving his new vehicle and undoubtedly appreciating the waves of his neighbours as he rode majestically past.

As evening wore on, and still he had not returned, Grandmother became increasingly worried about his well being — and would not rest until my father had been despatched on his bicycle to find out what ill had befallen her hero. When at length Dad found his father the old man was not in the best of tempers not the least of his troubles being the loss of face sustained in front of his friends, or the fact that he had been dressed up for the occasion. The old man's ignorance of this new-fangled invention — the internal combustion engine — had resulted in him flooding the carburettor and naturally the engine would not start no matter how much he wound the handle.

Dad recalled vividly his words to him when he arrived, words that seemed to us to sum-up the old man's philosophy on life, and his undying faith in his first love — "Give me an old engine and some coal and water and I'll always get home." He vowed never again to drive "the damn thing" and nor did he. From that moment on the official driver of 'The Car' was my father, who owing to his

59

engineering skill and the benefit of his training at the foundry was undoubtedly the best one suited to this purpose. He told me often of the change in their lives that came about by the use of the car, and how he enjoyed driving his father around, often visiting his various gangs at work either steam ploughing or threshing.

One story he related, and one that seems almost beyond belief today when considering the inadequacy of both the machine and the road surfaces of the day, concerned a trip he made to Dover. Dover lay some good distance away from the Romney Marsh, far beyond Folkestone, and would not normally have been journeyed to — even by train — the village communities of the day not venturing far abroad.

Nevertheless, Dad drove the car to Dover, to a dockyard I presume, to collect a complete hornplate for a Fowler ploughing engine. This engine was undergoing major repairs, possibly at the foundry — but if so why did he have to go to Dover for the part? I do not know the answer to this. He told me upon my enquiring how he carried such a large and heavy load upon the car that they merely folded down the hood and laid this heavy iron plate across it.

The mind races when one considers the rigours of the journey and the strong possibility of the load falling off or, worse still, shooting forward in the event of a sudden stop, even though barring collisions stops were not very sudden in the early Model T, to say nothing of the effects on the suspension of the vehicle. I am happy to say that no ills seemed to have befallen him on this escapade and he never remarked that he felt it at all out of the usual for that era. Fortunately they were not 'blessed' with today's traffic to contend with, but even then I would not hazard a guess at how long the double journey took to accomplish.

A delightful photograph exists showing my grandfather seated next to his eldest son — my dad — the driver, with his next son Len and their friend Jim Archer in the back taken presumably on a Sunday for they would have been at work on weekdays, just outside the Harvey Farm. As can be seen they were all wearing the obligatory headgear of the day and all smoking! The car was registered in 1921 by the Kent County Council as KE 914. I never heard of the eventual departure of this vehicle from their possession, but I am assured that it served them well for many years.

Opposite: 'The Car'. Grandfather Walter, driven by my father, with his brother Len and friend Jim Archer in the rear. Note the compulsory headgear and 'fag'.

Chapter 12

SEARCH FOR EMPLOYMENT

Being the eldest of eight children, during a not too prosperous era, it is easy to see how disillusion often struck home to my father. During his late teens he became increasingly aware of the inevitable outcome of his work for the family firm — despite the often repeated reassurances — "All this will be yours one day" and also "You know what you are working for." By the time he was a man courting strongly the girl he eventually married, and with the need to earn some substantial wages to enable him to save enough money to get married at a time when ten shillings a week was all that his father felt he could afford to pay him, an urge to seek other employment often came to him.

One such time occurred on a visit to the fairground at Rye. He and some friends found themselves, in much the same way as I do today, not admiring the riding machines, but gazing longingly at those giants that generated the power — the showmen's engines. Today my son and I seek out the Scammell generating lorries!! Whilst their gaze took in every detail of those throbbing machines, a man dismounted and spoke to my father, "Do you like it son?" he enquired, and naturally the reply was in the affirmative. "Could you drive it?" enquired the man, whereupon Dad's mates piped up, and told the man that "That's only a toy to what he's used to." Taken aback the man enquired to what they referred and was duly filled in with the details of the ploughing engines and such that Dad had cut his teeth on so to speak.

The man then invited him onto the footplate, where he could witness at first hand this gleaming machine working hard on the belt generating electricity for its corresponding attraction. Dad recalled that after a little while, during which time he told the man something of his exploits driving for his father, the man asked him to look after the engine for a bit while he had a break. Imagine his surprise when the man did not return for a few hours — leaving him in charge — whilst he undoubtedly was glad to have a few snatched hours rest.

When at length he did return, just as the fair was closing for the night, he asked Dad if all was well, and having been assured that this was in fact the case he offered him a job, saying "How would you like to come and join us as a driver then?" Agreeing to think it over and return the next night with his answer, Dad headed his bike for Brookland only to spend a sleepless night, so he told me often, tossing the offer over in his mind. The attractions of the fairground way of life, moving here and there, and driving a road engine appealed to him greatly, but I think the thought of the wrath of his father at being told of his leaving home and the pull of his girlfriend was sufficient to overcome his doubts, and he declined the offer.

He often said to me, "I wonder what would have been my life and what would have become of us if I had taken that offer?".

Another such incident was to happen some few years later during the general strike in 1926. Hearing that the Southern Railway was anxiously looking for steam engine drivers in a vain effort to keep their service going he presented himself at the Ashford Works. He told me that he was willing enough, despite the reaction of most of the populace to the contrary, to have a go. The thought of a larger salary and regular employment appealed to him and he went to sign on. The person he saw enquired where he had learnt to drive engines, and upon being told, refused him the job stating that he was sure he must be needed by his family in order to help keep them going equally as much as they also needed help.

This gentleman, whilst trying to be kind and helpful and conscious perhaps of the effect Dad's leaving his family might have had, was to be proven disastrously wrong. The family firm, like almost every other firm engaged in agricultural contracting at that time, were to suffer so harshly by the accumulative effects of the coal strike, followed closely by the general strike that year, that they never really recovered.

It was during the coal strike particularly, which lasted for six months, that persons turned away from steam engines and made do with other forms of power. The early tractors and cast off military vehicles gained a strong hold during this time and many, having made do with these, were content to carry on as such and never returned again to steam.

Chapter 13

TRAGEDY AT 'THE FLOTTS'

What started out as an enjoyable mid-summer day at the seaside ended with such dreadful consequences that it was afforded more than one whole page in the Kentish Express and Ashford News published on Thursday, 26th August 1922. The heading to page five of that issue reads: "Motor Coach Disaster, Calamitous ending to Ashford Outing. Trapped in Dyke by overturned car. Reeds in Ditch mistaken for road." Leaving Brookland the road to Rye and Hastings, the A359, runs fairly straight for the first mile or so and, as previously mentioned, in common with many roads upon the Marsh is bordered not by hedges but by deep well maintained ditches or dykes. About a half mile from the village the small bye-road leading to the Harvey Farm is set at right angles to the main road, which is reached by crossing a large culvert known as the Pinnock crossing. A further half mile and the road takes a sudden near 90° turn to the left, the first such bend of a complete zig zag in its course. The land on the farm side of this bend is known as 'The Flotts'. This area of land used to flood in wintertime, and to this stretch of water the youth of the neighbourhood would flock in frosty weather to learn to skate. Many including my father became quite expert at this sport. The problem of flooding in more recent times has been alleviated by the increasing use of land drains.

Many of the employees of an Ashford firm, British Saw Sharpening Machines Ltd, had set out early on the morning of Saturday, 21st August, for a day at Hastings. They travelled in two vehicles, one a large car, the other a much larger 32 seater char-a-banc. Returning in the evening, and approaching Brookland from Rye, the loaded char-a-banc led the car by some few hundred yards. This vehicle, typical of those of that era, was a 'toast rack' model, having seats in rows, each row having doors either side, fitted with a canvas hood, wooden spoked wheels and weighing some four tons.

The day had been fine and the evening quite balmy. At half past nine in the evening, it now being quite dark and with a ground mist rising, the coach came around the corner at the Flotts. What happened next must remain a mystery, but it is believed the driver mistook the reeds for the edge of the roadway, and ran his coach off the road. Realising this he stopped, but came to rest on the steeply sloping side of the drainage dyke, where momentarily the vehicle hung. Swaying quite slowly it slipped sideways until nearing the bottom the wheels suddenly came upon an obstruction, which resulted in the whole turning over completely, with the wheels in the air. The dyke at this point contained some 5 to 6 feet of mud and water and was of a width just sufficient to allow the coach to become firmly wedged across its bottom, resembling later as one of the rescuers remarked "A saucepan with the lid being put on." Only one person was thrown clear, the rest becoming wedged down into the water, and only able to free themselves by clawing away at the mud and escaping out from beneath the coach and from between the seats. Fortunately for some the hood, which had been folded back on the ride home, had the effect of keeping the rear of the coach higher out of the water and some were able to scramble free from this end of the vehicle, the others further forward not being so lucky. Many were trapped by the sides of the coach as it settled into the mud. The large car, a Vulcan, following came upon the scene after having been warned of the accident by three lady cyclists a few minutes after the event had occurred and rescue attempts started immediately. Someone pulled the tail lamp off the upturned coach and the sidelights from off the second vehicle were also used in an attempt to see what was going on. The horror of the occasion needs not much imagination to conjure up. The cries of the trapped and doomed passengers, together with the frantic efforts of the would-be rescuers, all this amid the rancid stench of the waters of the dyke, now mixed with the escaping fuel and oil from the coach and the acrid smell of the acetylene mixture from the headlamps of the submerged vehicle.

The alarm was quickly raised in the village and neighbouring dwellings and soon some 100 to 150 persons were on the scene, some bringing ropes and axes. The axes were used in a vain attempt to cut away the bottom of the upturned vehicle, but this proved futile on the heavy underside besides endangering those trapped inside. Eventually, around midnight, the coach was finally pulled over onto its wheels in the field by using the ropes and chains brought by the rescuers, and the last passengers were released from the swamp. In all eight persons including the driver had lost their lives, and many more were injured, some being crushed, and many with water entering their lungs.

The whole neighbourhood was filled with gloom at the news of the tragedy, all the more so for the fact that some of those who had lost their lives were veterans of the Boer War who had shown distinguished service to this country. The coach driver was Mr T. Crouch, whose family firm owned the vehicle, and who still run a coach hire firm from their premises in Ashford.

The Harvey Farm lies only a half mile or so away in a direct line from the Flotts and so it is not surprising that the family were some of the first to be roused after the accident. My Aunt Ethel, then a girl of eight years of age, well remembers the evening and recalls Grandmother taking the blankets from their beds to cover up some of the dead and injured passengers. For some reason Grandfather was out at the time of the accident and therefore it was Grandmother and one of her elder daughters that hastily lit the fire in the Wallis traction engine. It must not be overlooked that in those days no heavy breakdown vehicles existed locally with which to haul the upturned coach from the dyke, the family's traction engine being the nearest vehicle capable of rendering such assistance. One can imagine the frantic efforts put in by my family to raise steam quickly and the desperate glances that would have been cast at the pressure gauge on the old engine as they waited anxiously for the needle to rise. I am told Grandfather was fetched to carry out the task of raising the char-a-banc and all his skill was not sufficient to raise steam in time to help the trapped passengers. For he was on his way to the scene when the word came back that they had managed to right the vehicle by sheer manpower. However next morning he did go and pull the stricken vehicle up onto the hard road. The happenings of this event led to many questions being raised, even as far away as Westminster, about the increasing use of vehicles upon the high roads, and about the clear marking of verges and so on in areas such as this. The memory of that dreadful night also lives on not only in the ranks of my family, but also amongst those old enough amid many other communities over a wide area.

Chapter 14

WARTIME ON THE MARSH

Romney Marsh played its part in the six years of conflict during the Second World War. For its inhabitants life was to assume an uncanny air, for not only was it in the skies overhead that the panorama of the Battle of Britain was to unfold, but day to day life changed immeasurably.

Mostly below sea level, with a long and not easily defended coastline, and close to the continent, the Marsh was likely to be the area chosen by Hitler to launch his assault on Britain. Therefore the authorities set about preparing the inhabitants for this eventuality, and plans were drawn up to evacuate many of them. Thousands of the famed Romney Marsh breed of sheep were taken off the Marsh to higher land within the Weald of Kent and neighbouring counties, in an attempt to safeguard the breed. Everyone had to have an identity card with them at all times, and all were urged to carry gas masks.

The defence strategy in the event of invasion becoming imminent was to withdraw the inhabitants and to flood the Marsh, taking up a defensive line along the Royal Military Canal, which would thus at length have fulfilled the purpose for which it had been constructed over a hundred years before.

It can be easily understood that the dour, fiercely independent Marshmen, all men of Kent, did not take kindly to the idea, their only concession to war being that most built a dug-out shelter in their gardens, which whilst being a safe refuge in time of air raid, would have been little use had the ultimate deterrent of flooding been used. They tried as best they could to carry on as before, even though many, including myself and family were living out of a packed suitcase, under constant threat of having to evacuate at twenty-four hours notice should the invasion become a reality.

Until that day came many varied measures were taken to further fortify the Marsh and make even the infiltration of any troops as dangerous and treacherous as possible. All the dry ditches and dykes were filled with expanded coils of barbed wire. Blockhouses and concrete pillboxes were constructed at many points, as were tank stops and look-out posts. Pylons were built, together with aerials, connected to the newly invented radar system, and the latest in wireless techniques were also employed. Accompanying all this activity was the corresponding build up of military strength, especially later on just prior to the D-Day landings.

It is in connection with these troop movements that an incident happened about which I now write. Not long before the offensive was launched by the Allied Forces in Normandy, a large force of troops arrived one day in Brookland. By nightfall that day they had set up camp in the field next to the Harvey Farm — just through the garden hedge of the homestead — the field known as The

Tansey. My Uncle Ron recalled there were hundreds of them, so many in fact that in an effort to prevent his growing garden produce disappearing into their field kitchens, which had been set up against the garden fence, he told the officer in charge of the cookhouse that his greens and onions had been sprinkled with arsenic powder to stop the slugs.

For the next few days all was calm, with only one slight exception. This was that in spite of the blackout regulations a single light was persistently visible from a skylight in the roof of the nearby large house known as Poplar Hall. Despite frequent daily requests that this light should be put out, to which the occupants of Poplar Hall replied by denying its existence or by stating that it had been left on by mistake, nothing happened. At last, the military now devoid of patience, said that the next time the light appeared they would shoot it out. This seemed to work, it not being visible again.

It was either the very next night or the one after that, that the heavy drone of a lone enemy bomber was heard low overhead. My Uncle Ron, a young man in those days, sleeping in a small room next to his father's bedroom, recalled what happened clearly to mind. He states "This lone plane went round and round, up and down, low overhead, as if he was searching for something. By this time, my mother and all the rest of the family, except Father who said 'Nothing's going to get me out of bed — I never got out for Kaiser Bill in the First War, and I'm damned if I'm going to get out for Hitler in this one' — had fled to the dug-out in the garden. Round and round it went, for what seemed like ages, then all of a sudden there was an almighty explosion. Followed by silence — the plane had gone. Father remarked 'There now she's down, p'raps we can get some sleep'. This he soon did."

Next morning father and son went to inspect the damage. The bomb had dropped in a field some half a mile away from the farm and had left a huge crater. There was no sign of any earth from the crater not even enough to 'Fill a dung cart'. All that remained was a few mangled pieces of iron lying in the bottom. These pieces when laid on the ground resembled a ring of iron, something like a collar, and formed a circle the size of a forty gallon oil drum. Such was the power of an 'aerial torpedo'. Some earth from the crater was later found scattered over the ground clear of the main road more than a quarter of a mile distant from the point of impact.

Mercifully, the troops in the Tansey field were unharmed, despite the fact that the force of the blast had been sufficient to split the Harvey farmhouse from top to bottom, right up through the front door frame to eaves level, in the wall behind which father and son were in bed, and this in a house which was sheltered from the farm buildings which stood four square between the bomb and the house — a miracle indeed. It does not require much imagination to conjure up what might have been the scene that would have presented itself if only that bomb had been nearer.

Mystery surrounded that night's activity and the appearance of that lone bomber for years to follow. For it was not the sight of an aeroplane that was disturbing to the inhabitants, as they were an all too common sight, either singly or in multiples, but its appearance at that particular time, a few days after the large concentration of troops had arrived. Could its sudden appearance have had any relationship to that light that persistently shone out into the night air?

The answer to this question and to the intrigues that surrounded these happenings was to come many years later. After his marriage in 1946 Uncle Ron set up home in a small bungalow situated against the boundary wall of Poplar Hall. Whilst living there some tree cutters arrived one day to fell some large ash trees that had become dangerous by overhanging the road.

One of the men approached him one day, knowing that his home had been at the nearby farm and asked him if he could shed any light on a particular subject. What the tree cutter showed him left him feeling unnerved. Along the whole length of one of the felled tree trunks, and right up along one of its uppermost branches a slit had been made with a sharp knife. The bark had been lifted up and then wire had been tucked behind the bark, it being pushed back down into place. This wire led from the top most point of the tree, down the trunk, and was traced by the man across the ground right into one of the outhouses of Poplar Hall — an aviary type of building.

Reflecting on this he remembered the owners of the Hall at the time of the bomb had employed a servant with a foreign accent. Had he indeed been a German and if so a spy? Nevertheless, only a few days later the troops moved out as unexpectedly as they had arrived, and it was not long afterwards that Poplar Hall was sold, the erstwhile owners and their servants moving from the area.

The difficulties experienced by most persons living in that area during the war in trying to carry on their day to day lives as near normally as possible, were, if anything, more acute for my family than most. Being agricultural contractors, licensed by the War Agricultural Executive Committee from Sessions House, Maidstone, their lot was one of constantly moving from farm to farm even though restrictions on travel were in force at the time. This phenomenon led to some amusing incidents, one of which I feel illustrates quite clearly the spirit of determination that was prevalent at the time and which was obviously not lacking in my grandfather.

Having finished threshing in the Marsh he found that the next farm to visit on his list lay at a village beyond the Royal Military Canal. This had to be crossed at Appledore, one of the few crossing places which had not been blown up by our troops. It was reasoned that should an invasion of the Marsh have taken place it would have been easier to prevent a crossing of this waterway if only a few bridges remained. The chosen few, all major crossing points, had been heavily fortified with concrete pill boxes and the like, one of which remains at Appledore by the bridge. These defences were naturally backed up by a strong force of soldiers at each point.

The troops must have watched the old Ruston traction engine and threshing machine approach in full view for a considerable time, the land on the Marsh side of the canal being so flat. The road meanders about on its approach to the bridge, which was a hive of activity when finally the gang arrived. Grandfather was asked where he thought he was going, to which he replied, only to be told, "You can't cross the bridge with that" — a finger pointing at his faithful engine.

This would seem to have not been the right thing to have done, because tempers began to get short, whereupon an officer was called. This gentleman told Grandfather that he could not cross, and was told in reply that "Half of my living lies across that bridge, and so I'm going across." With that he nosed the engine onto the bridge and it was at this stage that he noticed the manhole covers in the roadway had been lifted and were lying ajar. Committed now he proceeded to cross and was not a little surprised to see that, as he did so, troops fled in all directions. Some appeared out of the manholes and dived for the safety of the pill boxes. In fact before he had completed his crossing not a soldier was to be seen anywhere. Only after safely reaching the roadway on the village side of the canal did the realisation of what had happened dawn on him. The Royal Engineers had been in the process of mining the bridge, and presumably not having finished their task and making safe all their land mines, they feared, luckily incorrectly, that the vibration set up by that iron shod old engine might have triggered off their mines. What Grandfather said about all this is not recorded, but I am told he did not seem at all ruffled by the imminent danger.

Another incident again illustrates some of the dangers and wry humour that also existed during the Battle of Britain for those trying as best they could to carry on normally. Mr Crow, a farmer at Stone on the Isle of Oxney, was a gentleman that the family visited annually on their threshing rounds. He was another famed for the quality of his cider. So good in fact was his brew that his foreman, a Mr Farrant, always appeared in a state that could not be described as sober. Alarmed that his cider casks seemed to empty more quickly that he felt they should, Mr Crow decided to keep the cider house locked. He told his foreman that when it came time for the threshermen to receive their daily ration of a quart per man he was to call for the key. This ration was indeed most generous, as no one was able to drink and work on a quart of Mr Crow's cider. Trugs Huggett used to fill his jar with his ration and take some home each day; there to build up a small stock for days to come. I am informed that Mr Crow never questioned the fact that even after the cider house was kept locked during the day, Mr Farrant still seemed to stumble about most of the time. The simple explanation for this was that, upon hearing of the intention to keep the casks under lock and key, Farrant took a length of hose and pushed it into the top of one cask of cider. The other end he pushed through the rear wall of the building, which was made of thatched hurdles, in order to keep the cider cool in summer, the end then being tucked up under the eaves of this small building. When the toils of the day, or the summer's heat, seemed too much for the foreman he would take down the hose, lie on his back at the rear of the cider house and suck the cider through the hose, safe always in the knowledge that it was to him that his employer entrusted the task of administering the brew. This also gave him the chance to change the hose from cask to cask as required.

During the family's visit to Mr Crow in 1940 when the Battle of Britain was at its height, the old Ruston engine blew some boiler tubes. These had to be replaced, which would have taken a day or so to accomplish. The decision was taken by Grandfather, in order to keep the gang busy, to thresh the stack of clover lying in the farmyard, whilst the engine was being repaired. It had been intended originally to finish the corn threshing first using the engine and Marshall drum, and then call up the clover huller powered by a Fordson Standard — 'John Henry' — afterwards. Word was therefore sent to the Marsh to give effect to the altered plan. Luckily the clover huller had just finished in a field not far from Appledore known as the 'Exhibition'. Arriving at Stone the gang duly set up and work commenced again threshing the clover seed.

Grandfather's youngest son, my Uncle Ron, then only a young man, was given the unhappy task of removing the offending tubes from the engine which stood in the open in the middle of the farmyard. Uncle Ron states that all went as well as could be expected, working as he was with a hammer and chisel in the restricted space of the firebox. His first job was to chisel off the beading around the ends of the failed tubes — this done mostly by feel as not much light penetrated the firebox, once he was ensconced therein. Oblivious to all that was going on outside he continued to hammer away, the hammer blows ringing in his ears, and filling his head to near bursting point. His thumbs and fingers ached from receiving a few missed blows from the hammer — something that was inevitable in the confined space in which he was working.

Suddenly, he still knows not why, he became aware of the sound of falling pieces of metal striking the yard around the engine. Alarmed at this he squeezed out from under the firebox to see what was happening whereupon he found his father standing at the back wheel of the engine. "What's the matter boy?" his father enquired, to which Ron replied that he had come out to see what was happening. Overhead a dog fight was raging — planes, some British Spitfires, others German, were weaving and screaming about the sky, all the while firing off their cannons at each other. The fierce battle was at its height immediately overhead. The spent shell cases were falling like rain, and it was these that had spattered around the engine while he worked.

Grandfather stood his ground and told his son "You get back under there, there's nothing that's going to hurt you under there." This he did, but not before noticing something that to this day brings a smile to his face, and something that illustrates that humour can be found in the most dangerous of situations.

Apparently, immediately the dog-fight appeared overhead and shell cases started to fall to the ground, near panic had set in amongst the gang, believing, apart from Grandfather, that they were all likely to be used as target practice. The foreman Mr Farrant, now, I presume, suddenly blessed with a clear head, had fled the stack to seek hasty refuge in some safe place — hastily followed by Trugs Huggett. On reaching the ground the nearest place of security — so they thought — was the dog kennel. The poor dog had already fled inside his house when suddenly his lead was pulled and he was dragged out, his space only to be occupied by the foreman. By the time Trugs Huggett reached the kennel it was virtually full — nevertheless he tried to get inside too, and managed only to get his head and shoulder in. Presumably, like the ostrich with its head stuck in the sand, he now felt quite safe. But the sight that presented itself to the world, and the frightened dog, not to say anything of the aeroplanes and their cannonfire was one that does not need much imagination.

Even the womenfolk were not safe from the dangers of war. Another incident that to the casual onlooker could possibly have seemed amusing, but which for the participants could so easily have ended with a fatal result, took place in the kitchen of the Harvey Farm itself. It serves well, I feel, as yet another illustration of the hazardous times through which all were passing during those long, dark days. In common with most every other kitchen in the land, at that time, the main source of cooking was conducted on a large, cast iron range. This was fuelled by a mixture of wood and coal, coal which, in the case of my family, came from the local coalman whose yard at Appledore Station, was naturally outdoors.

Returning home for their midday meal, one day, Aunt Ethel and the landgirls were met by an unusual sight. They presumably were either working in the farmyard or close by, as when out contracting, they carried their meals. Approaching the back door of the farmhouse, they saw all the kitchen furniture outside — funny, they thought. "I didn't know that Mother had the sweep coming or anything like that," Ethel said to her colleagues, but, upon entering the kitchen, all was revealed and soon explained — a scene of total devastation met their eyes.

Somehow, what was later thought to have been a live cannon shell, presumably from an aircraft and dropped in the coalyard, had found its way via a recent delivery of coal into the grate. Luckily for Grandma, who mercifully was out of the way at the time, it had exploded in the fire and in doing so had completely demolished it. Hot coal, soot, ashes and bits of cast iron had flown everywhere, to say nothing of the smoke which had blackened everything in sight. A thick curtain hanging by a rail across the back door, in an effort to keep the winter's ever present draughts at bay, had caught fire, but worse was to come for those hungry workers returning for lunch.

On a stone slab, between the sink and the copper, stood a small paraffin stove, on which a thin, wartime saucepan had been boiling a piece of brisket, the main ingredient of that day's meal. A splinter of the old grate had shot out like shrapnel and hit the saucepan, not hard enough to knock it off the stove, but enough to tear a three-cornered gash in it, which allowed all the boiling water and juices to run out, adding yet more hissing and spluttering noises to the pandemonium that had already broken out.

"We all had to buckle to and help Mother to clear up as best we could, and got no dinner that day," Ethel recalled.

Chapter 15

THE FAMILY FIRM

Even though my researches into the background and history of the family firm have been long and, as far as I have been able to make them, exhaustive, many details still elude me. It has proved impossible, with one notable exception, for instance, to ascertain accurately the dates when various items of equipment such as ploughing engine sets were purchased. Much of what transpired in those early days was conducted on a much more day to day basis than would be the case today, and as such was not documented. Obviously finance, or the lack of it, dictated the happenings and time scale of what took place and certainly no thought was given to the likelihood of anyone such as myself wishing to collate material at a later date, even if there had been the time to keep records. Indeed, as in any walk of life, much of what happened was deemed to be of no great importance to any outsider at the time, and the very familiarity of ploughing tackle meant that very few photographs were taken, which would have made my task easier, had they been available. My researches among Fowler records and other sources have however turned up some information that is worth documenting.

The overwhelming conclusion that I have drawn from this task is that like so many other small family concerns of that period, they were prey to circumstances beyond their control. Repeatedly throughout the years that steam was used many factors played an immense part in their day to day lives, often with disastrous consequences. Their fortunes rose and fell in a most alarming way, because of these factors, and yet this bore a direct relationship to the troublous times through which they passed.

It would seem that possibly the most stable and prosperous period in their history was from the turn of the century up until the first year or so of the Great War. The death of the firm's founder in 1917 however had a dramatic effect upon the viability of the concern. This was followed nine years later by the General Strike and in turn, by the Depression. An upturn came again, however, in the period immediately after steam ploughing ceased when threshing contracting became their major enterprise. This was to continue right through the Second World War and for my family, like many others, this six year period was to prove one of the best financially at least.

Nevertheless, from the firm's inception until the Harvey Farm was eventually sold, the family had to struggle, not only to give of their best service to the community in which they lived and worked, but also to keep their heads above water by dint of sheer hard labour, and always against a background of inadequate financial resources and of debts owing to them by the farmers for whom they worked. Farmers themselves often had insufficient capital to finance the work carried out for them and long credit was expected and given.

As mentioned earlier the firm was founded by Edward Newton at Wittersham in the latter half of the nineteenth century. The fine photograph, the most prized in my collection, used as the frontispiece to this narrative, shows quite clearly the first pair of engines used by the firm. I recollect having heard, however, that the very first ploughing undertaken by my family using steam power concerned the use of a single engine ploughing system, but this I have not been able to substantiate.

This pair of ploughing engines manufactured at the Steam Plough Works of John Fowler and Company of Leeds were supplied new to the farmers John Body and Son also of Wittersham, the same village as great grandfather in 1877. They bore a brass plate bearing the owner's name, village and stating that these were his No. 1 set.

Miraculously a most interesting document survives sealed with a sixpenny stamp being an agreement between John Body and great grandfather Edward dated 6th July 1891. It states that upon a down payment of fifty pounds on that day, and upon the payment in equal instalments of one hundred and twenty-five pounds on the eleventh day of October in each year from 1891 until 1895 the ownership of all that machinery listed in the schedule contained in this agreement be transferred from John Body to Edward Newton. The agreement contains several clauses dealing with such items as, keeping the equipment in good running repair: not removing the brass plate affixed until all payments had been made: informing the said John Body when asked where the equipment could be seen either stored or at work: the course of action to be taken upon default of any payment, or the bankruptcy of the hirer: the insurance of the equipment, and also states that upon the satisfactory completion of payment of all the instalments the ownership shall pass upon the further payment of one shilling. The schedule referred to reads: Two Fowler's 8 horse steam plough engines, Four furrow plough, Cultivator, Sleeping van, Screw jack, Portable forge, Anvil, Vice, Case of taps and dies, Tube expander, Small tools. By this one transaction therefore Edward Newton was able to establish himself as a steam plough proprietor, buying in instalments from his friend and near neighbour not only his first pair of ploughing engines, but also the tackle with which to go to work. How proud he must have been and how important also must have been that document to him, as it today forms one of only a small handful of such papers to have survived to the present day. This proves also I feel his faith in the future of steam ploughing as seen by him in 1891, remembering that six hundred and seventy-five pounds was a considerable sum to spend in those days, especially when the charge levied for ploughing an acre by this method had only reached 9d (3½p) in my own father's day the late 1920s and early 1930s. One can speculate also at his excitement, upon having paid his final instalment in 1895, in removing the former owner's plates and replacing them with his own. He must have kept one

Memorandum or Agreement

dated the   day of   One thousand
eight hundred and ninety one Between John Body
of Petersham in the County of Kent of the one part and
Edward Newton of the same place (hereinafter referred
to as the Hirer) of the other part

1   The said Hirer agrees to pay to the said John Body the
sum of Six hundred and seventy five pounds by the instalments
hereinafter mentioned for a Lease of or permission to use the
machinery and apparatus mentioned in the Schedule hereto

2   In consideration of such Agreement the said John Body
as the Owner of the Machinery and Apparatus mentioned in
the Schedule hereby authorises and permits the Hirer to use the
said Machinery and Apparatus for the term of Five years and
one quarter from the sixth day of July One thousand eight
hundred and ninety one, but subject to the terms and conditions
hereinafter expressed and which the parties respectively agree to
abide by and perform.

3   The Hirer having paid to the said John Body Fifty
pounds part of the said sum of Six hundred and seventy five
pounds (the receipt of which said sum of Fifty pounds the
said John Body hereby acknowledges shall pay the remainder
thereof by instalments payable as follows One hundred and
twenty five pounds on the eleventh day of October One thousand
eight hundred and ninety one, and a similar sum on the eleventh
day of October in each of the years One thousand eight hundred
and ninety two, One thousand eight hundred and ninety three
One thousand eight hundred and ninety four and One thousand
eight hundred and ninety five

4   The Hirer shall keep the said Machinery in all respects in
good repair and working order during the said term

5   The Hirer shall not remove or allow to be removed, but shall
always keep affixed to the said machinery during the said
term the plate or plates now affixed thereto, containing the words
" John Body - Owner "

6   The Hirer shall at all times when required inform the said
John Body where the said Machinery is stored or working.

7   If default shall be made by the Hirer for the space of Seven

of these plates as a talisman and souvenir, for it like the document itself survives and today forms one of my own collection.

Close study of the frontispiece I feel is warranted for it shows this odd numbered pair of single cylinder 8hp Fowler engines, being Numbers 3197 and 3365. The original photograph was believed to have been taken by the late much revered Major R.J.W. Ind. He was a great person for the set piece photograph, the one about which I write being a perfect example of his style. It was also by his way of thanking those concerned by giving them a print of his finished work, that this photograph entered the possession of my family.

I clearly remember a framed copy hanging on the wall of the front room at The Harvey farmhouse and being shown it with pride by my grandmother. Its significance to me is all important, for it portrays not only the engines mentioned, but also members of my family. Great grandfather Edward, the firm's founder, stands in the middle flanked by his sons: his eldest grandson, Walter, holds the oil can, another son, Fred, and daughter Grace stand on either side. The small boy standing close by his father is my own father Wilfred, then aged four. The season is winter — the house is The Harvey Farm — the date 1905. Further study of the photograph reveals certain damage to the print from which my copy was taken. This is because like many another front room of houses of that time, it was seldom used, even though the house would have been deemed overcrowded by today's standards. The fire was not often lit in that room, and the walls became damp; this affected the photograph, but it happily survived, to be used not only by myself, but by a number of other authors writing about events in that part of the country.

Returning to the engines they also warrant closer scrutiny. Completed on 2nd October and 2nd November respectively of the year 1877, they sport a few unusual features, the most notable being the rear wheels on the left hand engine No. 3365. I feel a little historical fact might help explain the reasons for their unusual appearance. Since the inception of steam engines, the makers of the day obviously were desirous that their machines would provide as much tractive effort as possible. Hence at first the driving wheels were often shod with straight across iron plates. These, as can be imagined, did little to improve the surface of the roads then in existence. The Locomotives and Highways Acts of 1861 and 1865 required the wheel of an engine to be in continuous contact with the road. Cross strakes at right angles to the T-Rings obviously failed to satisfy this condition. A continuous ring (as in a roller) gave insufficient grip, but the diagonal strake eventually formed a compromise. However, makers also tried out various other methods of achieving a good end result, at the same time keeping within the requirements of the acts. Thus we find two engines made within a month of one another shod in different styles. The difficulties to all this were eventually cleared up in The Highways and Locomotives (amendment) Act of 1878 which made diagonal strakes positively legal. Makers now adopted uniformity in fitting strakes with a 10° angle from the horizontal. This slight deflection was sufficient to allow a continuous band of steel upon the road, whilst at the same time provide much tractive effort.

Continuing my main narrative, it is with this pair of engines that the firm moved to the Harvey Farm in 1900. The firm then became titled as E. Newton Brookland, and a new plate bearing this legend is clearly visible attached to one of this pair of engines No. 3365 in the photograph on page 20. By this date also, Edward's growing sons, led by grandfather Walter, had reached an age when they could play a major role in the firm. Incidentally this pair of engines, the only 8hp ones owned by the family, remained with them right through to the end of the firm, receiving new boilers from the Oxford Steam Plough Co. sometime during 1919/20. This was borne out by the legend carried on the firebox doors, as also by the fact that they were fitted with Oxford type safety valves rather than the Salter spring balance type with which they were originally equipped. Whether they were re-boilered at Rye Foundry or Clarks Engineering Works at Ashford, I know not, but nevertheless the work was carried out. Later on after the acquisition of the 12hp engines, and my father growing in years, this was the set that he was to take over, when they became known by all as 'The boy's set'.

In all probability the next set of engines acquired was the pair of single cylinder 12hp Fowlers, Nos. 1199 and 1200 of 1870. This pair was new to R.J. Sankey the ironmonger of Ashford of 14th June of that year, later passing through the hands of R. Harnett of Birchington near Ashford. Again the date of acquisition by great grandfather is not recorded.

A further pair of engines of the same year, 1870, namely Nos. 1437 and 1438 of 12hp single cylinder construction was also supplied to R.J. Sankey of Ashford on 17th October. Mention has already been made of the fact that a Mr Sutton was foreman/manager for Sankey, besides which he was Edward's father-in-law. The late John Russell stated that it seems Mr Sutton eventually took two sets of engines, both 12hp singles, off Mr Sankey and ran them in his own account in the Sellinge area of Kent, a few miles from Ashford. No doubt Sankey realised that more money was to be made out of ironmongery and dealing in agricultural machinery than in steam ploughing. This judgment seems to have been accurate for we find that after a few years Sutton was in great difficulty. He robbed one set to keep the other going. Great grandfather advanced him money on the working set, finally taking them over. Their date of arrival at the Harvey farm, however, is not recorded, but believed to have been prior to 1910.

The fourth set of Fowler 12hp single cylinder ploughing engines came into the family's ownership in similar circumstances to those mentioned above, these being of 1873 vintage and numbered 1904 and 1909. They originally were supplied new on 9th May of that year to The Bowling Iron Co. of Bradford, subsequently passing to a Mr G. Henbrey of Playden near Rye. Mr Henbrey was the miller at Playden, and again another person who at first thought there was more money to be made out of cultivating than milling. Perhaps he was right until the bad times came, when he soon sold his engines, which by 1916 had come into the family's ownership. This fact is recorded in the engine register, kept at that time by their makers, John Fowler of Leeds.

These four sets, all venerable engines, and all with great similarity in their characteristics, were the ones that were used in what must have been the firm's period of greatest activity and growth.

It was during this period, however, that farmers in general were finding times becoming increasingly hard for them, with a corresponding effect upon the contractors upon whom they relied. It would seem the four sets only worked together for a very short space of time, possibly four or five seasons. By the time of the 1921 registration of vehicles, the family only had three sets in working condition, the last acquired ex-Henbrey ones already having been laid aside. In all probability this pair of engines never received a licence, at least my records do not record a licence plate being issued for either of the pair.

A local farmer to fall on hard times was a Mr J. Palmer of Appledore who found himself heavily in debt to the Newtons. Possibly being more christian than most and wishing to free himself of his indebtedness he struck a deal with my great-grandfather. This was that the family should take his Aveling and Porter traction engine No. 3069 of 1892 together with a Marshall threshing drum that was in his ownership. I do not know what value was placed upon these items or the size of the debt, but the engine and drum were in themselves not considered sufficient to meet it. Therefore it was agreed that the difference should be made up by the family taking the large square table upon which the bargain had been struck. This was how 'Tommy' Aveling came into the growing fleet of engines, and also how the family acquired a beautiful dining room table which unhappily was also sold when the firm finished.

It is worth recording, however, that the Marshall drum was of considerable interest in itself. Mr Palmer had it built by Marshalls of Gainsborough to his own specification with a six feet wide threshing drum. A machine of these proportions was a rarity in the United Kingdom, but I am told that many were made for export. The reason for its size was that Mr Palmer had threshed a good deal of corn for farmers in the Romney Marsh near Appledore and the fertile land in that area grew such long strawed corn that a wide drum was necessary in order to ensure that the threshed straw was fit for thatching. It must not be over-looked that in those days much of this land was being put under the plough — thanks to steam power — for the first time in its history. The fertility of this land, reclaimed from the sea, largely came from the silt which had been washed down into this low lying area from the rivers running from the higher ground, in the Weald of Kent. This fertility was thus being tapped for possibly the first time. Short strawed varieties of wheat had not then been developed as is the case today, when short strawed varieties of corn are the norm, and there was a market for long straw for use as cattle or horse bedding. It was by this transaction, therefore, that the Newtons acquired their first steam threshing outfit, and at the same time presumably a run of farms to visit with which to start a second and, eventually, a major part of their enterprise.

With the acquisition of 'Tommy Aveling' my grandfather was to take a bold step. This was to form a partnership with one Fred Dunster, his brother-in-law, who lived at Appledore. This partnership was solely for threshing, and at no time did Uncle Fred have anything to do with the steam ploughing business at the Harvey Farm. The engine was adorned with a plate, bearing the partnership name, Newton and Dunster, Appledore. The partnership survived for only a few years and ceased, as did all threshing activities, at the onset of the agricultural depression in the early 1920s.

It was a blow to the family when on 2nd June 1917 Edward's wife, my great-grandmother, died aged only 62 years. This grand Victorian lady, though she seemed aloof to most passers by and those who did not know her well, was in reality a person greatly loved by the family. She would seem to have been the one who kept her sense of values and order around which the Harvey family revolved as if a wheel.

It was a cruel twist of fate and a great tragedy which befell the family, when great-grandfather himself was taken ill and died suddenly following an operation at Ashford Cottage Hospital on 23rd July 1917, six weeks after his wife at the same early age of 62 years.

Thus it was that the now depleted family paid their second visit to the church of St Mary at Hinxhill in such a short space of time. They lie just inside the churchyard wall near the footpath that crosses to the church door, shaded now by the spreading branches of a mighty oak, which if only it could speak could tell such tales. It would be able to tell of an occasion much more joyous than these two recent events when a young agriculturalist brought his true love to this same church upon their wedding day in a different century, a wedding which was at the beginning of a road down which they were to pass, glimpsing on their travels many wondrous things.

The inscriptions upon the matching tablets to my great-grandparents state — on the one hand for Julia — 'Safe in the arms of Jesus' and on the other for Edward, 'Sadly missed, never forgotten'. How true these stone carved words are, as in delving into the past in order to write these words I feel as if I have truly got to know them. I am also aware now, even more, from whence my love of the steam engine — the ploughing engine in particular — has been handed down.

The lychgate to the church of St Mary at Hinxhill contains two small lift-up oak seats, one on either side of the pathway, but yet still under the roof. They are set in such a position as to be on the outside of the churchyard wall that abuts at the middle of the lychgate. Over the one are inscribed the words 'Rest for ye weary' and over the other 'In the land of the living'. Poignant this, I thought, on my last visit and yet so accurate, as on the inside of the wall is there surely not rest for those who have gone before?

Before the death of Edward, and during the hey days of work for the firm, a new title came into being. This owed its existence to the part played by grand-father and his brothers. Newly cast plates were now affixed to some engines which the firm owned bearing the legend E. Newton and Sons, Brookland. I do not presume to state that a proper constituted partnership as such was set up, but, possibly, merely a change of title for trading purposes. For, in common with many another, such details as would require the services of a solicitor were not often gone into.

Great-grandfather must have been a great character besides being a hard-working man. He had by his own enterprise carved out for himself and his family a special place in the community in which they lived. The firm started by him was known over a large area and even though there were several contractors at work in that locality, notably amongst them Blacklock's of Lydd, the Newtons seemed always to have had a lion's share of the work available to them.

He must have been a man much respected by his fellows as he became in turn a member of the Romney Marsh Board of Guardians and also a member of the local Rural District Council. A fierce streak of independence, often interpreted as defiance, was also a part of his make-up — this latter which was manifest also in his son and grandson — my grandfather and father. An amusing incident was told to me by my Aunt Maud, the widow of his second son Leonard, my god-father, which clearly illustrates the kind of man he was. It concerned the old man and the advent of what is known today as British Summer Time.

Aund Maud recalled that soon after her marriage to Uncle Len they were living in a house not far from the Harvey at Brattle and yet in a direct line to Brookland station. She well remembers great-grandfather walking to the station to catch the train to Ashford to visit the Corn Exchange where to conduct his business. He carried his small samples of grain in little sacks together with his bag of money, " 'Course it was sovereigns in them days". All this would be carried in a leather gladstone bag. He regularly caught the train on his many visits to town and market. He declared that he would have nothing to do with changing to British Summer Time when it was introduced and said he wasn't going to alter his clocks for anybody as he didn't believe in it.

The inevitable happened one day, however, and he arrived at Brookland Station, a good walk from the farm, only to find that he had missed the train by an hour. They did not hear any more of his stand against the clocks after that.

Like many of his contemporaries and, indeed, even his son who headed the firm after his death, he was loath to change preferring to do things the way they had always been done, and have no truck with new fangled ideas.

Nevertheless, his untimely death had a devastating effect upon the firm. So fierce was this that it never ever really recovered, and the repercussions were to change permanently the structure of the family's concern. For they were left much as a ship would be without a rudder or after the loss of a helmsman.

Grandfather (Walter) was now head of the family and he assumed the responsibility by leaving Elm Cottage and moving into the farmhouse at the Harvey. By now his family numbered six, my Aunt Ethel being but two years old at the time. Dave Cottington the blacksmith took up residence at Elm Cottage. The worst consequence of great-grandfather's death was that Walter's brothers and sisters all decided that they wanted their fair share out of their father's estate. Grandfather was left with the task of paying out each one, from resources that were already overstretched by his father's efforts to build up the firm, without winding it up to realise its assets. This task was to become a millstone to him and it is a tribute to him that he finally managed to achieve this distribution and at the same time keep the business going.

His brother Fred was given a portion of land next door to Elm Cottage on which to build a bungalow, using, I presume, in part his share of the money. Brother Arch took his and set up in a butcher's shop in Brookland, at the first outset, finally finishing with a blacksmith's forge in Rye, at the Landgate Tower, known as Tower Forge. Brother Sid elected to stay on the farm, but his preference for the four ale bar resulted in most of his share ending up in the hands of the local innkeepers. Walter's three sisters also elected to receive their share and £200 each was the figure that he had to find. This was by no means an easy task, bearing in mind the year was 1917.

Though his brothers had decided that for the most part they would go their own way, nevertheless, for motives that I can only assume were in case Grandfather achieved the near impossibility of expanding the firm, refused to break their ties with the steam ploughing business. They now termed themselves Newton Bros. and this is the title under which licences were issued to them by the Kent County Council in 1921, the engines being numbered from KE 6250 to KE 6255. The engines operated by the family during the war period already carried the oval County Registration plates, some clearly visible in the photos contained herein.

So little effort was put into the farm side of the business by his brothers that even their three cart horses at one time received so little exercise that they caught 'Stable III'. Grandfather then had to exercise them after returning late in the evenings after a full day's threshing. It even fell his lot to take the mare to visit the stud stallion when it was stabled at Old Farm, the next door farm.

It was during these few years immediately after the death of his father that the true value of the threshing partnership with 'Uncle Fred' Dunster came into its own. Even though this threshing gang had to provide for Uncle Fred's family as well, the little extra income it brought in those early days, coupled with the small returns from the steam ploughing, were enough to keep the firm going, if only just!

The family owed to my grandfather, Walter Newton, a great debt, not only for showing that rare quality of courage in the face of nearly overwhelming odds, but for keeping his family together, fed and clothed. Besides which he discharged those duties unfairly thrust upon him in full measure during the years that followed. My heart goes out to him for the obvious struggle that he had and surely it was only his indomitable spirit and sheer determination that pulled him through. Of all men that I have encountered to date he must rank as being one of the hardest worked men that I have ever met. As a small boy I would sit at his table a little frightened by him for he seemed most often gruff. And yet there was a twinkle in his eye from time to time and a sparkle in his face which I can never forget. His eldest son, my father, was to so resemble him in the years to follow, their features from the earliest of times being much alike. Looking back, reason suggests that he surely had no time to be happy and that his lot was one of toil and worry. I believe he had only one week's holiday in his entire life, yet I am convinced that basically he was a happy man.

As previously stated; I am led to believe that for one period in the life of the firm, obviously prior to 1921, all four sets of ploughing tackle were at work, as also was the threshing partnership of Newton and Dunster using the Aveling traction engine No. 3069. Busy days indeed, which unfortunately were not destined to last for any length of time. This assumption concerning the number of sets at work is borne out by a remark made by the late Chris Lambert of Horsmonden, a contemporary and friend of Grandfather, on 9th December 1944 that "during the last war they (the Newtons) worked four sets".

The onset of the 1920s saw a rapid decline in the fortunes of the farming community nationwide which, not surprisingly, was mirrored in another downturn in the prosperity of my family's fortunes. The most striking consequence of all this in the immediate vicinity of Harvey Farm, and indeed throughout the Marsh, was that farmers again turned away from the plough and returned to more permanent pasture. Presumably a farming policy based on grass and sheep, whilst in those days not in itself unduly profitable, was a cheaper system to run than an arable enterprise. At least now they had no bills from the steam ploughing contractors, even if they had the money to pay for them. The majority of farmers, however, were not even in a position to pay in full the large debts already incurred with the contractors with no hope of their ever being settled.

In common with some other ploughing contractors they continued to visit farmers year after year in a misguided attempt at keeping everything going, hoping to receive some payment off their account for past work. In reality they would have been better off staying at home, as they were only incurring greater debts and spending their own money into the bargain. Then the family began a period of years as black as any they were to face, and through it all Grandfather strove to keep going. His brothers, as previously stated, drifted away from time to time returning only to claim that which they had not truly earned. My father, for his part, married in 1925, had by 1927 set up home in a neighbouring village and was never to return for any length of time to the family firm. As the steam ploughing contracting dwindled, he tried to establish an income for himself from his small holding and duties at the Old Rectory, Snargate.

Quite quickly really, the fleet of engines became idle as, with no great amount of income, finance was not forthcoming with which to maintain the equipment. Rather was it a question of robbing one old engine to repair another. An indication of the harshness of the times and of the debts incurred by their former farmer friends is the fact that when my father ceased ploughing with his set of engines the family was owed £2,000 on his books alone, a vast sum of money in those days and, as previously mentioned, there was no hope of reclaiming such a

sum from the impoverished farmers. Little wonder then that my father and his brothers should leave the farm and seek other ways of earning a living.

It was in the early twenties also that the threshing partnership of Newton and Dunster of Appledore came to an end. Uncle Fred Dunster turned away from the Aveling and tried his hand instead at market gardening. This he did alongside the road at Appledore and a measure of success was his, people to this day referring to Dunster's strawberry field when passing through the village.

The Aveling traction engine was parked up at the hamlet of Wittersham Stocks where jt stayed in the open for over a decade until its rescue by Grandfather, narrated subsequently.

Opposite: 'All that survives'. The collection of engine nameplates on my study wall.

E. Newton — from off great-grandfather's first set of engines — see frontispiece photo.

J. Body & Son — a plate from off his No.1 set. This engine was sold to great-grandfather in 1891 on which he affixed the above plate (E. Newton).

R.J. Sankey No.1 and No.2 — one plate from each set of engines purchased by great-grandfather Edward from his brother-in-law, which became his own 2nd and 3rd sets.

G. Henbrey — one plate from Great-grandfather's No.4 set, which he purchased from the miller at Rye.

E. Newton & Sons — the plates affixed to engines at a later date, when Edward's four sons were of an age to work in the family firm.

Newton & Dunster. The one plate affixed to 'Tommy' Aveling during the time of grandfather Walter's partnership with his brother-in-law.

Chapter 16

OUT OF '20s INTO '30s

An indication of the way things were going in the country as a whole around this time may be obtained from another source, a study of which indicates the beginning of the end for steam ploughing. In February 1915, a body was set up known as The Steam Cultivation Development Association (S.C.D.A. in short). Its objective was simple; to promote the development and growth of steam cultivation, and it was set up by the implement manufacturers of the day. The reasoning behind it was that because of the 80 set order placed by the Ministry of Munitions for ploughing tackle in connection with the drive for home grown food production for the First World War, more work would be needed for these sets in time of peace.

It is necessary to remember that, after the initial surge of interest in steam cultivation that took place in the 1860s and 1870s and the subsequent saturation of the home market, virtually all sets provided from then until the Ministry of Munitions order for the Great War had been for export. On average only six sets per year had been sold to the home market during the preceding four decades. Maybe the manufacturers, like Fowlers, who quoted the life of their machines as being anything from thirty to seventy years, were in fact their own worst enemies. Of all the surviving engines the majority date from around the Great War era, with a few only surviving from the 1870 period and virtually none from the intervening years.

Yet in researching this book it came as a surprise to me to learn that the steam plough did not have a dramatic and lasting effect upon the arable acreage of the country. It is undeniable that the products of John Fowler undoubtedly made possible or made easier the reclamation of unused or derelict land, but it was primarily the price to be expected from the increased crops it grew that induced landlords and farmers to reclaim this type of land. The steam plough may have made it more possible but did not provide the spur. In fact the arable acreage of the country was at its highest point ever in the year 1871, standing at 14,946,000 acres. This acreage progressively fell until in 1915 it had dropped to 10,966,000 acres. The need for home food production during the First World War, as would be expected, then pushed this figure back up to 12,399,000 by the year 1919, it dropping back again during the years of the Depression to stand at only 8,935,000 acres just prior to the Second World War. Once more, with the country on a war footing, it rose dramatically to reach 14,523,000 acres by 1945. It would seem therefore that the humble horse was responsible for more than we are normally prepared to give it credit for. Undoubtedly though, as plant breeding and better

Opposite: Wintertime scene at Harvey Farm.

tillage of the soil got under way, increased yields more than compensated for the diminished acreage.

The S.C.D.A. had a register of Subscribers and Donors, all engine owners being asked to subscribe, for the common good. Their book No. 3 covers the period 1927-1932 and is dated March 1927. In 1928 it lists 145 members representing 288 sets of tackle in the United Kingdom. By January 1930 this number had dropped to 128 members with 268 sets, and by September 1932, 131 members with only 238 sets, a measure of the decline that had set in so far as steam cultivation was concerned. The rapid growth of cultivation by the expanding numbers of internal combustion engined tractors no doubt had played a large part in this, the mass-production of Henry Ford's ubiquitous Fordson Standard taking more of the blame than most.

A lone significant entry as far as I am concerned, in the Register of the S.C.D.A. dated 18th July 1931, shows a subscription of £1.00 being paid by Newton Bros., Harvey Farm, Brookland, Kent. This presumably meant that by that date only one pair of engines from their fleet was at work.

Thus it was that the twenties gave way to the thirties, which found Grandfather struggling on. This was achieved by a little steam ploughing being done from time to time, and this was the situation that existed for a number of years around that time. Once free of the depression in 1932 things at last began to look a little brighter at Harvey Farm, if only a little. What little steam ploughing was done was mostly carried out by one of the 12hp engines matched up with one of the 8hp engines formerly in the set run by my father.

In an effort to up-date some of these old 12hp engines, a conversion was carried out at the farm on the steering mechanism of a few. The old tank-type steering with all its inherent dangers and shortcomings was done away with, the more familiar worm driven steering being adopted. This work was undertaken in the workshop at the Harvey.

The members of the family, both boys and girls, were often called upon to lend a hand as labourers both at this time and in the years to come. Indeed, some of the girls worked as hard as a good many men, particularly in the threshing gang. Walter's brother Fred, so I am told, was the man who got the old 8hp out of retirement. He boarded over the tender floor and, even though the engine possessed a cracked high speed pinion, she was put to work.

Steam threshing also began to raise its head once more, even though this had never quite ceased during those dark days. This had been carried out using the elderly Wallis and Steevens 6hp traction engine No. T164 of 1882 coupled up with a Marshall threshing drum.

It was around this time that the Fowler gyrotiller began to appear in that part of the country. In fact it was after one of these machines had been used that the family carried out its last steam ploughing task, this being 1936 or possibly 1937. Saddlers Wall field was again the scene of this event, strange to tell, but by this time it had changed hands and by now was owned by my mother's eldest brother, Fred.

It was Fred Apps who called at the Harvey and asked if they could do something with his field, as he had had it gyrotilled and now could do nothing with it. In fact this was a good demonstration of the failing of these machines, as their very downfall came about because they literally stirred the ground up too much.

So it was that Grandfather and his brother Fred took their ill-matched odd pair of engines to this field only a short distance from the homestead. At first they tried to plough the land, but were unable to do so. The gyrotiller had so upset the structure of the soil that it would not flow through the plough. There was now only one option open to them and that was to cultivate the land.

My Uncle Ron, by this time a young man, either in his last few weeks at school or having just left, told me he rode on the cultivator with his Uncle Sid. He states that the ground was so soft that the cultivator rode through it — the frame resting on the surface — the tines completely submerged.

Once again in the closing stages of their steam contracting business, that had been started all those years before, that jynxed field nearly claimed two more victims. Riding across the field on the cultivator he kicked at clods of earth and rubbish that from time to time came over the frame. Having been told by his Uncle to stop doing it, he nevertheless, as young boys are wont to do, resumed his activity after a short while. All of a sudden it happened — he missed his footing and slipped down between the frame of the cultivator, the passage of earth beneath his feet having the instant effect of dragging him down under the frame. His uncle, unable to signal to the engine to stop, left his seat and putting his arms under his young shoulders — the frame by now having reached his waist as he was being dragged through the ground — he pulled him back out of the ironwork against the flow of the earth. How he did so Uncle Ron still does not know and it needs not much imagination to picture how soon it would have been before his chest and then his head would have become crushed by the heavy frame of the cultivator.

Before the field was finished another incident happened which might to this day serve as a warning to all engaged in similar occupations, or when using wire ropes. As stated previously, the cultivator, owing to the bottomless state of the ground, was travelling at full depth. This naturally put a great strain on the steel rope, especially as these had not been used much in the immediate past, but nevertheless were thought quite sound.

Suddenly the cultivator hit a piece of ground that had been missed by the gyrotiller, with the result that it stopped dead. The resultant strain on the engine rope was such that it snapped. This was witnessed by my Uncle Ron who states that "it recoiled like a snake, and shot up into the air, standing right up above the engine, before falling as if in slow motion to the ground". Luckily no one was injured in this incident, but it illustrates the dangers hidden in using ropes of this nature. The rope being used on this occasion was an old one; one which had all the tension taken out of itself by constant use. Imagine if you will, the recoil effect of a much newer rope and the dangers that lie therein.

So it was that the steam ploughing era of my family came to a close. It was not long after this, a matter of a year or two, at the onset of the Second World War, that the first engines were cut up for scrap. It strikes me as sad to think that possibly this was inevitable, as a complete era in the farming way of life was obviously passing by and drawing to a close. Moreover I cannot help feeling a further pang of sadness that all this, started by my great-grandfather and carried on so doggedly by his eldest son, should not go out in a blaze of glory, but rather wither away as it were — a far cry from the earlier days when Great-grandpa Edward used to receive his ploughshare and cultivator points by the truckload at Appledore station!

'The' Bondcutter. Aunt Ethel (grandfather's third daughter). Taken at the same time as the next picture, April 1942. The photo comes from a snapshot which was carried in the wallet of Ethel's husband Tom, throughout the North Africa campaign during the Second World War.

Chapter 17

THE THRESHING ERA — 2nd TIME AROUND

At the outbreak of the Second World War, in common with all other agricultural contractors, the family firm now found themselves under the Ministry of Agriculture, Fisheries and Food. They were registered and a field of operations was mapped out for them. Each firm was given a list of farms on their quota that they had to visit, where they were required to carry out threshing duties.

The female population of the country again was mobilised, the land army coming into its own, and what valiant service was performed. It was decided at the Harvey Farm, just as during the First World War, that it would be better to have the land girls assigned to them living in, rather than have them billeted at Brenzett, a few miles away from the farm.

Thus it was that three strange, though pretty faces joined those gathered around the meal table in that farmhouse. The reasoning behind this decision was that it was far easier to run a threshing gang with all the members being local to the farm, than would be the case if some lived in another village. The very nature of their business, which was so dependent upon the weather, consequently often demanding quick decisions, made this imperative. The gang could be quickly assembled when a break in the weather came, which would not have been the case if journeys had had to be made to round them up as it were. Also early morning starts were more easily accomplished if all started out from the same place.

Even though the land girls lived in, they still came under the watchful eye of the local land army inspector. Their wages were paid by Grandfather who was reimbursed by the Ministry from Sessions House, Maidstone, to whom also were all records sent as to the work carried out and the number of sacks of corn threshed from each farm visited.

Each threshing set had four girls, a driver and a feeder for the drum. Therefore the set from the Harvey consisted of Grandfather, driving the Ruston, Trugs Huggett to feed the Marshall drum, the three aforementioned land girls, and my Aunt Ethel, Grandfather's fifth child. Ethel's husband, Tom, was away in the army, where he served in the Tank Corps with distinction. Aunt Ethel was not so lucky as the land girls, however, being designated by her father as a regular land worker and registered as such. This unfortunately meant that she did not fall under the same wages scheme as the other girls, but rather was paid by her father out of his earnings, he not being reimbursed for her efforts. Therefore, it needs only a little imagination to see that when times were not too good, as happened periodically, Ethel was often the one to suffer, her wage being the last consideration.

Nevertheless, the yeoman service put in by the girls led by Ethel, who was renowned over a large area for her exceptional skill as a bondcutter, was deserving of the highest praise. They became fiercely loyal about their employer, and they were much loved by my grandmother. These girls worked often from daylight to dark, seven days a week, and became in every respect where muscle-power and skill was called for equal to, if not better, than most men. Many of these land girls had no experience of farmwork or even the lifestyle of country folk prior to being sent to their respective employers. The service rendered by them nation-wide has been well documented and deservedly so. With the country on a war footing, employment abounded for the threshing gang and the Ruston engine was never cold. In one year during the war we believe this gang set up an all-time record. Out of fifty-two weeks in the year they threshed continuously for forty-seven of them, returning only to the Harvey Farm during the second week in July having set out on their rounds in August of the previous year.

To most persons not familiar with the agricultural scene of that part of Kent this would not seem possible. Normally one assumes that cereals are the only crops threshed. This is not so — as in these parts all manner of other crops were grown in those days, turnips, swedes and mangolds were grown for the seed, besides peas, beans, tick beans and so on, each job seemingly more dusty than the rest, but each one equally important.

During all this time Ethel continued at her job of bondcutting, (cutting the string around the sheaf and handing it to the man feeding the drum). She tells of being forever told by her father, "Don't you let those bonds go". Should any string or bonds have been let to fall into the thresher, there was the danger of their becoming wound round any piece of the machinery. This would mean that a stop would eventually have to be made to free the machine, which inevitably meant lost time. Bearings could become hot if wrapped around with these bonds, which could lead to fire, a very real risk in the stackyard.

The farmers also would pay a premium to the bondcutter if he or she could save the strings to be used again for tying up the necks of sacks of corn. String, like most other commodities in those war days, was in short supply and consequently dear to buy. They would pay sixpence a day (2½p) to the bondcutter if the strings were saved and even ninepence (3½p) a day if they were saved with all the knots at one end. This might seem frivolous, but to achieve the latter each sheaf had to be turned round to place the knot uppermost before being cut, which naturally made the already unpleasant job more difficult. It was during this time also that both boys and girls of his family were pressed into helping man the threshers and join the gangs as time permitted. Even his sons together with son-in-law when on leave from the services would lend a hand, anyone and everyone to keep the thresher going. So important to the family's well being was the safety of their

Opposite: 'The Threshing Gang'. Photo taken at Fred Kingsnorth's farm, Tillery Lane, Brook-land using the Ruston traction engine and the Marshall drum. Standing l to r — Bert (Trugs) Huggett, landgirl Grace, Bert Arter, Grandfather Walter (exhaling cigarette smoke), Aunt Ethel, Fred Kingsnorth, in front Harry Hickmott, landgirl Betty, Stan Arter (Bert's son).

threshing machines that Aunt Ethel, together with her older brother Jack, would be despatched prior to darkness on their bikes to wherever the machine was currently at work. Their job was to sit with it throughout the long dark night to ensure its safety, and the safety of the crops, whenever an incendiary bomb raid was about. Such was the spirit that prevailed throughout the entire country during those dark days, and yet it was himself that Grandfather pushed the hardest.

So it was that given this long consistent period of full employment, albeit under difficult conditions, that again a measure of prosperity returned to the family. This was helped along in no small way by the tremendous effort put into the family firm by Grandfather's youngest son, my Uncle Ron. For now free from school and equipped with the Standard Fordson 'John Henry' and armed with the Ruston Hornsby clover huller, he too was able to work side by side with the threshing gang, when the occasion arose, also undertaking a considerable amount of work baling. A measure of their joint success must surely be that it was during this time of war that Grandfather was at last able to free himself of the debts that had dogged him, since the death of his father, and the subsequent burden placed upon him by his own brothers and sisters. Not only did he succeed in doing this, but he was also able to pay off the mortgage on Harvey Farm. At last he felt he had achieved something and attained his goal, how proud he must have been as he walked those acres and gazed at his implements and live-stock. No man surely was deserving of more praise than he for his efforts which had led to its just reward.

The end of hostilities brought with it a change in the life of the family. Steam engines were used no more — Grandfather, now nearing his seventies, took a less active role in the running of the farm and contracting business. His son Ron, now equipped with a Fordson Major tractor, assumed control, and to him almost imperceptibly fell the task of bread winner.

Opposite: A happy day at Brookland Church, 6th July 1946. The marriage of Uncle Ron to landgirl Gwen (Boxall) which brought the Newtons out in force. Ron is the youngest of grandfather's eight children who farms at Parish Farm, Brookland, from where he carries out the family trade of agricultural contracting. The author stands with his brother behind the pony's head, whilst father Wilfred stands extreme right.

Chapter 18

ODDS AND ENDS

During my chosen task I have called to mind many odd stories and tales told to me as a small boy by my father. Some of these I have already set down, others seem to fall into no set place within these pages, but are worthy of recording. I feel this to be the case as if not documented they are likely to be forgotten and lost. They form another small cameo picture in the folk lore of the era about which I write, but I do not presume to suppose that they in themselves are in any way unique — many old steam plough men could easily have recounted such tales. For what they are worth I now set them down.

Ploughing one particular time in the early '20s my father's gang was on the extremity of its rounds down in the Marsh. As usual he was driving one of the old 8hp singles. For a few days they had cast their eyes over the hedges in the distance to where they could see the chimneys of a pair of engines at work belonging to one of their rivals — a ploughing contracting concern that also worked down in the Marsh, believed now to have been Holmwoods of Newchurch. I am told that each day they kept a close eye on this pair, even seeing who could start first in the morning and pull the last furrow at night. Not only were they concerned at keeping up with their rivals, but they were also fascinated by the sight. These engines were compounds and were fresh to their owners, either as second-hand machines or brand new, I know not which.

At last curiosity overcame them and they decided to knock off a shade before dark one evening and walk over and have a look at these unfamiliar engines, telling themselves as they went that no way could they be better "than our old singles". Quite why the events that followed happened I am not sure. Maybe it was due to one of the drivers trying to impress these onlookers with his prowess. Nevertheless he managed, just as darkness fell, to wind the plough right up into the flywheel of his engine, breaking it all to pieces. This may seem impossible to the uninitiated, but in reality is really quite an easy thing to do, as with an anti-balance two-way plough one whole set of furrows is in the air as it approaches the left hand engine. It only needs the driver trying to get that little extra ploughed before stopping to pull the plough and the result can be quite catastrophic. Fowler K7 No. 14738, photographed when owned by Holmwoods of Newchurch, is believed to be the victim of this incident.

My father also recalled as a young boy before his teens not only seeing the very earliest type of 'flying machine' that often frequented that flat area of land,

Opposite: Fowler K7 No. 14738 1917, in the ownership of Holmwoods of Newchurch. — Photo taken by J. Russell in 1935.   (Copy courtesy of L. Burberry R.L.S.)

but also another event. He was taken by his father to witness a secret ploughing demonstration. This was to view a piece of machinery that was doing experimental trials on the heavy ground of the Marsh. What they in fact saw I never quite got the answer to — was it a Darby Digger, I wonder?

Dad would also get very incensed if I, or anyone else for that matter, referred to the stovepipe on an engine as a chimney. "CHIMNEY?" he would say, "Chimneys are for houses and factories, engines and ships have FUNNELS". This terminology surely owed its existence to the nearness to the sea that they all lived, but I must confess, try as I might, I can never get used to calling this object by any other name than a chimney!!

In mentioning the nearness to the sea, another often recounted anecdote comes easily to mind. In the long hot days of summer, was it surely not a special breed of man that could stand on an engine all day? Dad would recall that sometimes on a still day when there was no wind, or especially if the engine was behind a hedge, it would get so hot in the tender that even to touch the fire irons one had to use a rag to hold them. He stated that sometimes whilst the rope was running out from his engine with the plough moving away, he would get down and stand in the edge of the water in the ditches that often ran round the fields. In climbing back ready for his next 'pull' he said the steam used to rise up from his boots and legs. Riverlets of perspiration would leave their traces amid the coal dust down his legs he would recall, stating often that it was a wonder that old ploughmen never suffered from bad legs as a result of all the heat, but they surprisingly did not — at least not more than any other hard worked man of that era. He said they often felt sorry for the poor carter and horses drawing water ceaselessly to the engines all day under those conditions.

If it so happened that they were working near the coast, especially around Lydd-on-Sea just off Dungeness, they would, beside trying to catch the local pub just before closing time as they were wont to do after a hot day, sometimes go for a swim in the sea.

Dungeness in those days was an even more fascinating, if more remote, place than it is today. During the last war further concrete roads were built across the shingle to enable this part of the coastline to play its part in the war effort. It has been well documented that it was from here that the pipeline under the ocean, PLUTO for short, stretched out across the sea to feed petrol to the hungry engines of the D-Day assault. Two gutted bungalows housed the pumping machinery — ideal camouflage from enemy planes. In the era of which I write no such luxuries as roads were evident across the miles of shifting shingle, the constantly changing coastline being first eroded and then replaced by successive tides and the winter storms. Then the most numerous inhabitants were the birds that wheeled and dived about the sky, their song the only noise other than the swish of the sea as it first pounded and then slipped back from the pebbles on the beach. In fact the first concrete road to traverse part of the wilderness was only of single track and was laid by Lydd council in 1925 as part of a scheme to help the unemployed in those difficult years.

Fishermen were the only human participants in the drama of life on that inaccessible corner of England, men who knew well the fickle tides of those treacherous waters made deep by the relentless sea. Two families, the Oillers and the Tarts, more than any other lived on that remote landscape and then, as now, they manned the lifeboat in which they would put to sea to help others, their wives and womenfolk helping to launch the boat, often in some of the worst weather to be found anywhere around our coastline. To cross this shingle in those days one could hire large wooden shoes, fastened with a leather strap similar to snow shoes worn by the Eskimos in far off Alaska. These were known as 'she-bats'.

Equipped thus the inhabitants would trudge their way across the shingle to where they lived carrying any shopping they might have in large baskets on their backs. Many of the houses on that part of the shoreline were made from old railway carriages from the South Eastern and Chatham Railway purchased from Ashford Works during the '20s and early '30s for as little as £10 each delivered to site. Many of these still survive. Most houses would have been tarred all over to protect them from the fearsome winds and weather which swept the exposed coastline in times of storm. So it was to this intriguing spot of land that ploughmen betook themselves as dusk fell and put an end to their labours for the day. Once on the seashore they divested themselves of their work-stained clothing and plunged into the cooling water to soothe away the aches from their tired limbs. Today's terminology would doubtless refer to this as skinny-dipping, but in those days they had only the birds and fish for company.

Refreshed from their swim they would make their way to one of the two inns to be found in Dungeness. One was the Britannia, situated near the point, now re-built as a low single storey structure easily battened down in winter. It still sports a horse-drawn cart as an exhibit of times past. This cart is unusual in having wheels made up out of large diameter barrels each one some five to six feet in diameter and with a bearing surface of approximately two feet. This was the way in which fresh supplies of beer and all other essentials were drawn across the shingle. The large wheels prevented the cart from getting bogged down in the loose surface.

Most often the men would make for the other inn, the Pilot, this one much more famous and full of intrigue. This inn, whose main structure in those days consisted of a large portion of an upturned sailing boat, had not only atmosphere, but a folklore all its own.

This area, latterly immortalised by Russell Thorndike in his tales of the legendary smuggler, Dr Syn, has by its very proximity to the Continent and open nature of its shoreline been the haunt of smugglers down through the ages. It is not surprising therefore that the Pilot inn, situated within hailing distance on this remote coast should offer its customers, or at least those not suspiciously like customs and excise men, fare of more unusual kind than that normally offered in like establishments of more inland situation. Dad recalled that when asking for a tot of brandy say, a code existed as to how one placed one's coinage on the bar. The landlord would enquire "In or Out" to which the person in the know would answer accordingly. 'In' meant drinks and tobacco from our native country and via traditional suppliers, whereas 'out' meant smuggled goods devoid of any excise duty.

Today things have changed — no longer are drinks and tobacco freely if a little cautiously smuggled in — most likely a boat load of illegal immigrants would be the cargo. The Pilot has gone and in its place a modern public house, devoid of any character either materially or architecturally has risen; the only similarity being that it carries that same haunting name.

Another tit-bit concerned my father at a much earlier age — when only a young schoolboy. As mentioned in the opening pages he suffered from asthma and like so many fellow sufferers he was also afflicted with eczema, a nasty, unsightly skin disease which seems to go hand in hand with asthma, and one which is particularly unpleasant in young children.

In an effort to bring light relief to his young life, he would often during the long summer school holidays be sent to the market town of Tenterden to spend a holiday with his maternal grandparents, Mr and Mrs Williams. I am told Mr Williams was a little man and that his wife was also of small stature. He was a schoolteacher, and a lay preacher — 'a chapelman'. He dressed in black clothes and wore a flat saucer-shaped 'preacher-style' hat. This couple were good to him and he enjoyed his holidays in their company. His little steps would often lead him to the Tenterden town station where on 'The Farmer's line' he would watch the steam engines carry all manner of goods on this single line railway. It is little wonder that these engines should interest him, as steam engines had been part of his existence since his earliest memories. This Robertsbridge line, known as the Kent and East Sussex Railway, is now one of the major tourist attractions in the South East, the preservationists being justifiably proud of what they have achieved in only a handful of years.

Whilst staying with Grandma Williams on holiday, he went with her to answer the door of her house in Tannery Lane. A gypsy stood on the doorstep selling pegs. She could not help noticing the young boy with his arms all bandaged up in an attempt to stop his scratching himself. Upon enquiring what had befallen the young lad, the gypsy lady was told of his ailment. She told Grandma Williams that she would return on the morrow with something to help him. This she duly did — her remedy — an ivy leaf potion. This was applied to his arms and soon the skin healed completely — the trouble never to return. Once more I feel that this demonstrates that nature surely provides a cure for all ailments, if only we can find or know the ingredients. Maybe we would all learn something from those folk who live closer to nature than we ourselves.

Chapter 19

TRACTION ENGINES

'The Wallis'

The firm of Wallis and Steevens of Basingstoke, founded by Arthur Wallis in 1856, was second only to Messrs Aveling and Porter of Rochester for the number of steam vehicles manufactured by firms south of the Thames. Like most firms of general engineers at that time, they put their hand to manufacturing all manner of items requested of them by the local farming fraternity. It was natural, therefore, that when the steam engine raised its head they should be amongst the first of those to grasp this new form of motive power and produce their own designs.

Curiously, and at variance to their contemporaries, they adopted a most unusual numbering pattern for their products, not numbering each item in an ascending numerical order but giving each separate type of engine a different prefix. This method was employed by the firm for a good number of years and was not to change until after the celebrated engine designer William Fletcher had left their employ in 1878.

Sales of steam engines by their manufacture were recorded in their engine register. These leather bound books amounting to two volumes were contained in a leather box secured by a leather strap with a brass buckle. Page 144 of volume 1 records that engine No. T. (for traction engine) 164 was tested on 5th August 1882. It also records that this was carried out for a Joseph Standing of Charlswood.

With a refreshing innocence and honesty, unhappily not often found today, but in those days was more common perhaps, the beautiful hand-written document also quotes the further details.

'The engine made to standard dimensions, as per drawings — but the tank is a small one (their plates were ordered smaller in mistake from an old list). Front and back wheels machine made, boiler machine made (good one). The first one turned out of hand, since we had rivetters. Hind wheels 5'6" diameter x 15" width on drawing 1846 with side view as drawing 38, from outside to centre of spud holes 9½".'

This 6hp single cylinder traction engine was therefore unique, as hitherto the boilers for all engines had been hand rivetted. The reference to the boiler being a good one and the error over the tank being catalogued adds, I feel, a very human touch and an air of Victoriana to the proceedings.

Turning to the firm's sales ledger and account book for the same era, we find further mention of this same engine, namely 'Engine as standard throughout,

with a slight alteration to pressure gauge and whistle pipe which is made 6″ from flange to centre. Firebars made ½″ shorter than ordinary'. It then lists details as to the number and dimensions of these fire bars. It would seem, however, that the first person who used the engine, the aforementioned Mr Standing, possibly only hired it for a short period of time, a not uncommon practice in those days, or so I am told.

The records then note that T.164 was supplied to Mr Benjamin Chart of Horley, Surrey on 5th April 1883, a further item of interest being that it was supplied to this gentleman together with a threshing machine of their manufacture, a 54″ A.3 model. These two items were paid for by the farmer over a period of two years, he paying in total the sum of £537 or thereabouts. Wallis and Steevens sold a good many engines under hire purchase agreements, many of which returned to the works owing to default on payments.

It would seem that this little engine moved about a bit for we find that by 1896 it was owned by a Mr E. Bellis of Flint Mountain, Flintshire. By the time of vehicle registration being established in 1921 it had returned to the south coast area, The West Sussex County Council records show that a registration number of BP 6299 was allotted to the engine at that time when owned by a Major A.E. Lerwill of Wisborough Green.

The date of purchase of this engine by my family is unhappily not recorded; some slight contradictions existing in the records in my possession. It was believed however to have been purchased by my grandfather in 1928 at an auction at Haslemere, the price of £50 reflecting the well worn state of this engine. It says much for the products of this Basingstoke firm that upon acquisition by the family it was again to continue to work hard as contract threshing increasingly became the mainstay of their business. It worked out of the Harvey farm with Grandfather as driver in conjunction, for a short while, with the Aveling 'Tommy' driven by Uncle Fred Dunster at Appledore.

As explained elsewhere, with the onset of the depression contract ploughing declined dramatically upon the Marsh. Thus it was that the fortunes of the family being on the shoulders of the threshing gang, and the inevitable reliance upon the Wallis. With the folding up of the threshing operation at Appledore after a few years it was to the Wallis and its gang that even more befell the task of keeping the firm going. This situation existed well into the thirties until the Ruston Proctor appeared upon the scene, believed to be at the end of 1934.

The photograph of Grandfather Walter driving his Wallis shows what a fine state the engine was in, although by then it had been at work 50 years or more, despite the slight imperfections! Grandfather was very proud of this engine, saying always with affection, providing you had plenty of coal and water it would do anything asked of it. Some measure of his prowess at driving this engine can be gleaned from the fact that once when endeavouring to extricate himself and a threshing machine from a particularly muddy gateway the engine reared right up. Unfortunately the cotter pin holding the front axle to the perch

Opposite: The 'Wallis' No. T164 of 1882 6 NHP. Grandfather on his favourite steed in characteristic pose.

101

bracket had fallen out unnoticed previously, therefore the engine upon rearing left its front axle and wheels on the ground in the mud. Grandfather held the engine aloft with the controls, whilst his gang lined up the axle once again. Steadily he lowered the engine down, right into its correct position where it was coupled up and made fast. I am told he did not seem at all ruffled by the experience.

By the outbreak of the Second World War age had presumably begun to take its toll on the Wallis because, once the Ruston had been repaired, it was never to work again. Another photograph shows it lying disused at the rear of the forge awaiting its fate, which was to come in 1939.

'Tommy Aveling'

The record sheet, now held at Grantham by the successors of Aveling and Porter of Rochester, shows that engine No. 3069 was despatched on 13th August 1892. It was a single cylinder two speed 6hp agricultural traction engine weighing 8 tons, 9cwt 1qtr and supplied new to J. Cox of Egham, Surrey. Further notes indicate that it was in the possession of Henry Coombs of Bagshot on 27th February 1899 and at some time later in the hands of a Mr James Palmer of Appledore, in the county of Kent.

The story of how the family acquired this traction engine, affectionately known by them as Tommy, has already been documented. However, on the demise of the partnership of Newton and Dunster, it was left parked up at Wittersham Stocks. The engine and threshing machine were left in the open and stood there for more than ten years, at the end of which Grandfather decided to bring it home. He intended to use it again on the Marsh, as things picked up and more work began to come his way.

Thus it was that he and Trugs Huggett cycled to Wittersham one day to start getting the engine ready. Unfortunately they found that the unusual six feet wide Marshall drum had begun to deteriorate and so it was decided to leave this behind. In fact it never worked again, staying where it was and finally rotting out.

They set to work on the engine, cleaning it out, repacking the glands and so on. For two or three days they busied themselves thus. Trugs Huggett told me that "Ron was only a small boy then, yet he pedalled all the way up to Wittersham to see the injun — on his fairy cycle." He also stated "The cylinder would not move so we kept levering it with a bit of wood to get it free" — "next day we put a fire in it, to warm her through."

The following day they decided to get it home to the Harvey. All went apparently well until they descended a hill down towards the Marsh when the chimney fell off and rolled down the road in front of them. I am told that during the years that it had stood rust had set in, nevertheless they found some wire and wired it on again. By the time they had reached Appledore Bridge it

Opposite: Wallis and Steevens traction engine T 164 of 1882 6 NHP Reg. No. BP 6299. Salter safety valves and cross arm governors clearly visible on this early single cylinder engine — Photo taken circa 1935 by J. Russell. (Copy courtesy of late T.B. Paisley)

had become so dark that they had to leave it on the roadside for the night, bringing it home the following day. This feat was recalled by many persons at the time who marvelled at the manufacture of a machine that could be left for so long and yet with the minimum of maintenance be got going again. After arrival at the Harvey the old engine was re-tubed with tubes supplied by Messrs Thurlows of Stowmarket, and put to work, its first task after repair being threshing for a Mr Hobbs, at Fairfield Court, Brookland. So it was that Tommy Aveling became a mainstay in the life of the family, a role which is shared with the venerable Wallis and Steevens traction engine. For a few seasons they worked in harmony with their respective threshing machines.

During these years of re-birth for Tommy, age seemed to take its toll particularly in the firebox, which cracked and was repaired on the farm by a metal patch being fixed over the crack, secured by extra long stays. This in turn during a particularly frosty snap also sprung a leak, which necessitated it being welded. When finally again this also leaked the engine was left where it stood and was never again to steam. Its resting place was a few miles from the Harvey Farm, on a piece of waste ground alongside the road at Bowdell Farm, Snargate, the farm at which it was working when the leak occurred. Sad to say I never did see this engine, being only a young boy at that time, I suppose I never got to Bowdell Farm on my infrequent visits to my grandparents. Yet here was an engine about which I was to hear possibly more than any other during the years that were to follow. It lay on this site from about 1938 until, in common with all the remaining fleet, it was eventually cut up at the final clearance of the firm in 1952.

Miraculously the brass plate from it survived, bearing the legend 'Newton and Dunster, Appledore'. This was given to me by my Uncle Ron and is now one of my most prized possessions. The affection shown by members of my family and past employees for this fine and also long-suffering product of the Rochester works is probably best summed up by the remark made by Trugs Huggett after having been shown a photo of this engine. He studied this for a long while then reluctantly handing it back said with a voice full of emotion "She weren't half a nice little thing".

'The Ruston'

The well established and renowned firm of agricultural engineers of George Thurlow and Sons of Stowmarket, Suffolk placed an order with Ruston Proctor of Lincoln for a type SH 8hp single cylinder traction engine on 20th February 1907. This engine was to be of a stock pattern with usual fittings and with ordinary finish, and instructions were issued that it must carry a nameplate of J. Higgins and Co., Bonnington, Kent. The aspect of this that amuses me in these modern times is that with an order placed on 20th February, delivery was required for 1st March of the same year. Nevertheless, the engine was supplied via Messrs Thurlow and Sons on 11th July 1907.

Opposite: 'Tommy Aveling' T.E. No. 3069 of 1892 6 NHP KE 6690 Kent County Council licence plate No. 176. — Photo taken at Bowdell Farm, Snargate, its final resting place on 30th November 1944. (Copy courtesy of J.P. Mullett)

J. Higgins and Co. of Bonnington were, as were my forebears, agricultural contractors, and I suspect that the two firms often met on their respective boundaries, as both Bonnington and Brookland are situated on the Romney Marsh if some few miles distance from one another. Higgins had several engines and I possess in my collection a set of photographs of one of their sets of ploughing tackle at work just after Armistice Day 1918.

By all accounts the firm worked the Ruston, numbered 32404, very hard, as the records of its makers show many spare parts being ordered from a date of less than a year after its manufacture. Indeed on 2nd July an order was received for a new crank and countershaft bearings, Thurlows stating on behalf of the owners that the originals were cracked. Subsequent to this new bearings in crucible steel were sent from Lincoln.

Further evidence of hard work is given by the need of a new chimney on an order placed 15th September 1909, but maybe an accident involving a low tree might have had something to do with this. I wonder if the owners felt that in this engine they had one of rogue manufacture because the replacements needed over a period of 15 years that it was in their ownership were numerous, a whole sheaf of order forms from the spares department at Lincoln bearing witness to this.

The replacements needed besides those already mentioned included such items as a new Bevel gear locking plate, a new low pressure piston, a new water lift, a new smokebox ring and indeed a complete differential gear. However I understand that in common with many other traction engines supplied by virtually all makers, when driven carefully and considerately by their owners, few troubles resulted. This is not the sort of result however obtained by an average owner using employed labour. Messrs Higgins case is therefore not untypical of the period.

Whether patience was lost by the firm or not I do not know, but by 1922 this engine had been sold to farmers much nearer the Newtons' field of operation, namely T.W. Paine and Sons of Lydd. The significance of this to my story is that for many years my grandfather had carried out threshing for Mr Paine. He visited his farm annually, on his regular run of farms, and was at a loss to know why all of a sudden one year he was not required. The story goes that Paines, believing that there was obviously money to be made out of contract theshing, bought their own set of tackle, the intention being, or so I have been told, that they would carry out their own threshing and then do that of their neighbouring farmers, and in this way take some of the more distant trade from the regular contractor — Grandfather. It cannot be denied that there is an advantage in having one's own set of tackle, as one can thresh when circumstances prove best for oneself, and not have to wait for the contractor to call on his rounds.

When news of this filtered back to Harvey Farm, things, as might have been expected, were not happy as these were difficult times for all, and they, like all

Opposite: Ruston Proctor T.E. No. 32404 1907 8 NHP KE 6254. Stands awaiting repairs after arrival from Paines of Lydd. — Photo taken circa 1935 by J. Russell.
(Copy courtesy of late T.B. Paisley)

their contemporaries, relied very much on visiting the same farmers year in and year out. No amount of loss of trade — however small — was welcome — and this after many years of friendship between the two principals concerned was indeed a bitter pill to swallow.

However, nothing could be done about this situation and for a year or two they paid no visit to the farm at Lydd. What finally happened to reverse this predicament I do not know, except that I recall my father saying that Mr Paine called on Grandfather one day and asked him to go again and do his threshing. Also I believe there was mention of a lack of an engine driver, or at least one with sufficient skill to keep the engine running and properly maintained. Delighted at the news Grandfather took his set of tackle to Lydd with all haste and duly did the job in question. Before they left his farm Mr Paine — now I presume happy again at their restored friendship, and with the way things had been done — said to Grandfather, "The best thing you can do Walter is to buy that engine off me and use it yourself." Whereupon a deal was struck and the engine changed hands again.

My father comes into this episode of my tale, as it was to him the lot fell of driving the engine home. It was decided that when the threshing gang had finished at Mr Paine's farm the two sets would travel in convoy in order that an eye could be kept on the Ruston in case help was needed. Dad duly arrived at the farm and prepared his steed for the road, filling her up and oiling round as necessary. It must be remembered that the engine had been lying idle for a considerable time and even though the journey back to the Harvey was only about seven miles, a certain amount of apprehension was felt regarding the impending trip. Was not this apprehension a kind of sixth sense on his part, as the short journey that ensued he was never to forget, or was it merely just the reaction of a prudent man to taking an untried and partially derelict engine onto the road.

Besides the engine, the transaction that had taken place included an old Clayton and Shuttleworth threshing machine with which Mr Paine had previously carried out his work. This was, even though not very sound, taken along, presumably under the reasoning that if left without any machine of his own, in future the previous owner would have no option but to use a contractor — hopefully Grandfather! Incidentally, the threshing drum was never used by my family, but remained at the Harvey where it rotted out.

It was early on that autumn day when at last the fire was lit in the Ruston and final preparations were made before taking to the road. Grandfather led the way, driving his venerable old Wallis and Steevens, Trugs Huggett steering and Dad following singlehanded on the newly purchased engine, this bringing the family's traction engine fleet up to three in number.

Opposite: The 'Revived' Ruston — repaired ready to do further yeoman service during the Second World War. The last T.E. used by the Family Firm. Note: smokebox door and chimney taken from off one of the disused ploughers — the number plate shown is incorrect! — Photo taken circa 1944 by D. Chamberlain. (Copy courtesy of late T.B. Paisley)

He told me often, with the sharpness of recollection that follows an event in one's life that leaves an indelible imprint on one's mind — such as that short in distance but long in time journey — "That old engine leaked from everywhere it possibly could," — the glands leaked, the injector leaked, and worst of all the tubes leaked, bearing witness beyond doubt to its previous owner's unsuccessful efforts to find a regular and competent driver.

Try as he would he was unable to keep up with his father, the aged Wallis, being well maintained, striding out for home. Even though he had started out with a tender full of coal, this was rapidly consumed in his efforts to raise sufficient steam to keep going. Frequent stops were made for water, wherever it could be found, as with leaking tubes the pump had to be left on continuously, even this expedient proving often inadequate, when the injector would also have to be employed.

Anyone who has been either fortunate or unfortunate enough to drive a steam engine will know only too well how fine a balance has to be struck between water level, steam pressure, and the brightness of the fire. All will also know of how easy it is for this balance to become upset which can have the most dramatic effect on any journey. This is sometimes the case with the most experienced of drivers, even when driving a well maintained engine. Even the state or type of coal used can radically change any journey, and have a most dramatic effect on the steaming capability of an engine.

At length it was decided that Grandfather should go on ahead leaving Dad to struggle on as best he could with the promise that help would be sent out to him as soon as they reached home. This duly was done and he finally reached the safety of the farmyard well after dark. Again Trugs Huggett told me in recounting that particular day's happenings "Your Dad couldn't catch us with that Ruston, that old Wallis really could travel you know". Unfair this, I thought, as the protagonists upon that day never started out on an even footing.

A photograph taken by the late J. Russell in 1935 shows the Ruston standing side by side with the Wallis, presumably in much the same state as it had appeared upon arrival from Paines. Records exist, bearing my grandfather's name and dated 15th December 1936, showing that spares were ordered with which to carry out certain repairs to the engine — including a new set of tubes. These repairs were carried out in the workshop on the farm, at which time a new chimney and smokebox door were fitted. These items were taken from one of the old 12hp ploughers — the ex-Henbrey ones. As mentioned previously, they were the first ones laid aside and accordingly robbed prior to being cut up just before the outbreak of the Second World War. By all accounts from that date onwards the Ruston seems to have lost its gremlins — because it worked with Grandfather, becoming his favourite engine, right up until he ceased using steam. It was also the last engine used by the family in connection with its business and was for a good many years the only one in a steamable condition.

Curiously, although the engines used by my family were affectionately referred to as 'The Wallis', 'The Ruston' and 'Tommy Aveling' none were ever adorned with a brass nameplate acclaiming such titles, as would obviously be the case today in preservation.

Chapter 20

THE CONTEMPORARY SCENE

This then was the face of the Harvey Farm that presented itself to me when, as a small boy, I spent an eagerly awaited holiday with my grandparents. The journey from Berkshire to these inhabitants of the Romney Marsh, who referred to the Royal county as 'up in the Shires', was in itself an adventure for a young lad. Most often I would be taken by my father and mother to Hungerford station some six miles from my home at Coombe, on the Chalk Downlands, there to catch a local train to Reading. This steam hauled stopping train was a real feature of the locality — a friend to all — with a folklore all of its own.

Reaching Reading, still accompanied by Mother, I would wait with eager anticipation for the connecting train. This one was much grander than the local train — a main line monster: 'The Birkenhead Express'. A seat would be found for me in a carriage with a kindly looking woman occupant who would be asked to "keep an eye on the boy" and "please to make sure he gets out at Ashford and not before". Saying farewell to her offspring after the usual caution of "Make sure you are a good boy and behave yourself", Mother would depart, leaving me alone in this adult world not only full of strangers, but steam engines galore. Three stops later I would duly be met by my relations who would escort me the twelve miles to Brookland and the Harvey Farm. This day long trip would finally end with me being tucked up in bed in a little room just off my grandparents' room over the front door. There in unfamiliar surroundings I would be thinking back over all the excitement of the day, and finally succumb to sleep enveloped as it were in the warmth of a feather mattress — there to dream of the morrow and the days that lay ahead.

Breakfast would be consumed at the worst of a rate the following morning, in my haste to explore the great outdoors. Inevitably it would be to the area on the far side of the farm buildings that I would head for first, there to see the line of rusting engines about which I have written much, and to compare the sight of these again with my previous visit. Not only the engines which would appear to be more dilapidated than before, and sunk a little further into the soft earth, but also the machinery with which they worked so tirelessly would receive a careful scrutiny. The three living vans, now devoid of any occupants, would still be along the roadside, parked just off the road surface along the verge, as if waiting impatiently for the call to service again — a call that was not to come.

In and out of the now silent forge and surrounding buildings I would dart and play. What marvellous playthings these strange and silent monsters would become to an adventurous boy. How I wish now that I had known, or even been aware at that tender age, of the part played by these machines in the life of my family. Oblivious to all this, I would carry on regardless and yet this scene was

all the while being indelibly etched upon my growing mind. So much so that today, many years after their demise and that of my kindly grandparents, I can recall that scene as if in a picture.

Days spent there were happy times and many small recollections exist which bring immense pleasure to mind, such as walking over the fields in company with Grandfather to look at the sheep, intrigued all the while to watch him as he walked with the ever present thistle spud in his hand. This combined tool and walking stick was alien to me and yet he was so adept at using it, when with a quick flick of the wrist the offending thistle would be chopped out of the ground. In reality it was nothing more than a small spade-like piece of metal attached to the end of a long straight walking stick. Every journey taken on foot from the farmhouse into the fields would see him armed with this, as before the days of spray chemicals and more modern farming techniques, thistles were an ever present nuisance in the permanent pasture fields, which, if close by the farmstead, would most probably have been down to permanent pasture for perhaps hundreds of years. It is surprising how easy it was to keep these weeds under control by this most simple of methods, whilst at the same time looking after the well being of one's flock. The 'thistle-spud' had its own place against the farmhouse door, this I believe being commonplace in most farm dwellings in that area during those days.

Sometimes our walks would be in the form of an inspection of the crops, tick beans, potatoes and so on. On other occasions my time might be taken up by helping to pick up potatoes during their harvest, when my pocket money would be supplemented to the tune of ½d a bag for every one filled, this paid out by Grandpa at the end of a long day. I smile to recall the sight at one such harvest time of the old horse that pulled the potato spinner; one that would not go backwards without much cajoling and pushing. When on this particular occasion the reluctant beast finally agreed to do so, he would not stop and backed the potato spinner right into the ditch that bordered the field. Imagine Grandfather's delight at this!

Teatimes had a special fascination for me, as the family gathered around the large kitchen table at the end of a long hard day. The warmth of the kitchen fire and the glow of the oil lamp which sat four square in the middle of the table, bathing the hungry diners in a flickering light, had a magical effect upon me. Besides Grandpa and Grandma who sat at the far side with their backs to the fire, there would also be other members of the family, my aunt and uncle, a cousin and the landgirls amongst whom and between whom I sat.

The day's work would be talked about; the girls who had been out threshing on some neighbouring farm would excitedly tell of any gossip, trials or tribulations that they had heard or overcome. Until his marriage my Uncle Ron, as the head of the threshing gang, would tell his father of the job in hand and the state

Opposite: 'As I remember them'. Awaiting their final fate — taken circa 1950 outside the workshop at Harvey Farm. Nearest camera 12 HP single 1870 — then the pair of 8 NHP Nos. 3197, and 3365 of 1877 — at the rear ex Henbrey 12 NHP singles 1904 and 1909 of 1873.
(Copy courtesy R.L.S.)

of the crop being handled. The old man would listen intently, as I also did, and then would enquire when would it be finished and to whom would they be going next? After his marriage and leaving home, Uncle Ron would always poke his head around the door to report thus to his father. This sight always enthralled me, as more often than not his face would be almost totally covered with dust from his hard day's labour at the rear of the threshing machine.

Sometimes when seated at tea there would come a knock at the door. Grandma would answer this to find 'Pat' standing there. Pat was a wonderful sight to me and seemed to be not only slightly mysterious but at the same time a little frightening. "Have you got a can of tea for Pat Missus?" he would enquire. Whereupon the darling woman would take his old tin and fill it to the brim with steaming tea. A large slice of bread and cheese and a lump of cake would also find its way to the doorstep, and he would be told to spend the night in the warmth of the barn or stable. Pat was a gentleman of the road, Irish by birth, a man gentle of nature, who frequently visited the farm and who eked out a living by fruit picking, potato picking and so on for the local farming community. He would leave the area after a while and reappear as mysteriously and suddenly as he had left it, at a later season. This life-style intrigued me greatly at the time, but I could not help a shiver running up my back when the door was shut behind him, and thinking of him being out there in the dark — me being in the warmth and bosom of my caring family.

Sometimes another knock would come on the door. This would signal the arrival of the baker's van, who having almost finished his rounds for the day would be on his way home to Rye. Grandma would follow him out to the road-side where often by the light of a candle she would purchase her bread and cakes. It was no little surprise to me that even at this late hour he would invariably happen to have a 'spare' chocolate gateau which she would always buy. In fact she was of such a soft and endearing nature that I am sure traders often took an unfair advantage of her generosity, and many times persuaded her to buy more that she ought. She would return laden to the warmth of the kitchen where she would tell Grandpa that "it seemed a shame to let the man take these items back to Rye". Possibly my love of chocolate gateau stems from these incidents.

Such was her gentle attitude to all creatures great and small that even a tame duck that was supposed to live with the rest of the flock around the orchard adjacent to the stream and pond would follow her around like a dog. This duck, named Alice, would waddle along behind her as she went to the clothes line, the garden and such like, and was even seen in the kitchen from time to time.

Of such stuff as this is the warmth of my memories made — memories of loved ones who helped shape my life. By their example and tenderness we who have been privileged to live if only for a short and fleeting moment in their shadow have been greatly enriched by the experience.

Sadly this charming and graceful lady was to leave us in 1951 and life at the Harvey was never to be the same again. Grandfather, as has been previously stated, remained at the homestead, now being cared for by his youngest daughter,

Grandfather Walter Edward Newton. Taken at the rear of Harvey Farmhouse a few months before he died in 1961, in his 81st year. Behind him on the wall a nameplate from one of the engines; it reads: E. Newton and Sons Brookland.

Sybil. His role now was of semi-retirement, the farming, contracting business and day to day running of the firm being in the capable hands of his son Ron. With his lifelong partner now no longer at his side and his beloved engines silent it would seem that his days were often long. His mind must often have strayed back over the years to the hustle and bustle of days which were far from empty — days which, in their time, were so full of life, when not enough hours of daylight existed in which to accomplish all that had been undertaken, days when the sound of exhaust beats up the chimney were mixed with the ring of steel gearing in his ears, over all of which was the smell of hot oil, steam and smoke. As the last of those lorry loads of iron that had been his engines disappeared out of sight on their journey back to the scrap yards of Lynch of Strood he must have felt a pang of regret and sadness.

Not long after the death of his mother, my father finally persuaded Grandpa to spend a few days with us 'up in the Shires'. Dad drove down to Kent and brought the old man home with him. I believe this was the farthest he had ever travelled in his life. He journeyed not far from the Marsh in ordinary times, paying only an annual visit to Tenterden sheep fair. At one of these I believe he struck up a friendship that was to last for a great many years, with another champion of the steam engine — Chris Lambert, of Horsmonden. I was told often by my father that he enjoyed his visit to Berkshire — strange to tell the hills fascinated him — so different to his Romney Marsh. His visit was made more eventful no doubt for being able to see the areas and terrain over which his eldest son — my father — had worked with the large A.A. Fowler ploughing

115

engines during the reclamation of the estate on which we lived. He would have been able to marvel at the undoubted skill he had imparted to his son, in his teaching to him of the art of driving a steam engine. But even he had to admit that he would not have wanted to drive these large machines over some of the downland that had in fact been reclaimed.

His holiday lasted ten days, after which he returned to the Marsh to resume his role as head of the firm — if now, only as a figurehead.

My parents, my brother and I visited as often as times would allow and he always delighted in showing us around as in former years. One photograph I have was taken of this grand old man of steam only a few months before his death in 1961 when he was in his 81st year. He is seated in the lean-to glass porch at the rear of the farmhouse under a nameplate affixed to the wall above his head. This nameplate, rescued from one of his ploughing engines, bears the legend 'E. Newton and Sons, Brookland'.

My grandparents' grave is situated just inside the wall of Brookland churchyard, at a point in which the wall seems to jut out towards the Harvey Farm some mile distant. Sheep now graze this churchyard and tend the graves, keeping the grass as short as any lawn. Like those of many another local family the mortal remains of my much loved ones now lie safe within the shadow of the church, which has played a great part in the lives of this community, adjacent also to the small village school which to this day still echoes to the laughter of children at play, much the same as it did when the children of those who sleep were pupils within its walls. I find it a strange but somehow comforting thought to muse over the fact that sheep now tend and care over those who in life had spent so much time and effort in watching over the well-being of their flocks — a strange paradox this!

Having mentioned earlier in these pages of my home being in Berkshire, a few lines I feel are necessary to relate the reason for my family moving from the Marsh. I have stated that my father, in order to enhance his position in life, had left the farm at the demise of the ploughing contracting business. He had sought employment at Snargate — the village of my birth — some few miles distant from Brookland. Whilst we were living there the war began, bringing the Battle of Britain in 1940. Snargate, like much of the Marsh, lies well below sea level, and so was one of the areas which were marked to be flooded had the invasion, which all deemed imminent, become a reality.

The lives of the inhabitants of that area can be easily imagined. For ourselves, at one stage my mother, brother and myself were evacuated to stay with one of my mother's elder sisters at Aylesbury in Buckinghamshire. This journey by train throughout the night is still vivid in my mind even though I was not much over two years of age at the time.

On our return to Snargate things soon had taken a turn for the worse with the onset of the Battle of Britain. Much of my brother's and my time was spent either under the kitchen table or else down in a dug-out shelter, which had hastily

Opposite: 'After they had gone'. An aerial view of the Harvey Farm, Brookland, taken circa 1953. The forge, workshop and last resting place of all the steam equipment can be clearly seen in the foreground.

been dug by my father in the garden of our bungalow home. Many days and nights were spent there sleeping on old car seats covered by blankets. Even then it was steam ploughing engines that more than Hitler were destined to change the course of our lives.

In an effort to free his family from the worst of these dangers, and the ever present threat of immediate evacuation, living as we were out of suitcases with the knowledge that we might have to leave our home at any time at twenty-four hours notice, my father anxiously scanned the pages of 'The Farmers Weekly'. In one particular issue an advert caught his eye, which read, that a farmer was seeking a person to take charge of a reclamation scheme to bring back into agricultural use a large estate that he had recently purchased in Berkshire. The farmer in question was the revolutionary and inventive A.J. Hosier, the estate being at Coombe on the Berkshire Downs. This 1,500 acre site had for the previous 100 years or thereabouts been run purely as a sporting estate by the previous owners. Most of the land which could have been cultivated, as well as the hilltops, had been left to grow wild. Many of these acres were by now covered by scrub, gorse and woodland. With the war effort well under way, and with the Ministry directive that all available land had to come under the plough to help the drive for home food production, it was imperative that this land be reclaimed. The mainstay of this reclamation work was to be the use of a pair of A.A. Fowler compound ploughing engines.

My father went to Berkshire, met Mr Hosier, looked at the task in hand and said that if he could persuade my mother to live in such a hilly district he would undertake to do the job. My mother readily agreed, saying she would live anywhere as long as it was relatively safe and that the family could be together. We therefore left the Marsh and duly set up home in Berkshire in the March of 1941, Dad having already started employment in the late autumn of 1940, living in with a family whilst a cottage was repaired for us.

The pair of engines arrived quite soon after we had set up home, having been bought by Mr Hosier from John Allen and Co. of Oxford. They were numbered 15252 and 15253 and were named, I believe by Dad, Energy and Progress.

The reclamation of this estate and the work undertaken by these engines has become something of a legend in these parts; not only because these were some of the last ploughing engines to be used in this locality, but also because of the method employed. The estate took in the Roman Tumulus of Walbury Hill, which at 975 feet above sea level is the highest chalk down in the south of England and this fact alone serves well to illustrate, I feel, the size of the task undertaken.

Certain details of this work appeared in the book 'Hosier's Farming System', published in 1951. Following the successful reclamation of the estate my father was asked to manage the farming enterprise for the owner, which he did most

Opposite: My father driving Fowler AA7 compound No. 15253 of 8th February 1918 Reg. No. BW 4636 on a hillside at Coombe, near Newbury, Berkshire, following the initial reclamation of the estate using steam power. My brother and I are in the tender, my mother looking on — photo taken in 1942. Engine Nos. 15252/15253 supplied new to The Oxford Steam Plough Co. — then via John Allen and Co. to Hosier — scrapped in 1951.

Snapshot taken same time as the previous picture by Dad — my brother and I on the cultivator and Mother driving.

successfully until the estate was finally sold in 1956. The large part played by my father in all this and the role of the Fowler engines could possibly one day be the subject of another story;

Returning to my main narrative I must relate the sequence of events that was being played out at Brookland. Uncle Ron had, during the intervening years, become romantically attached to one of the attractive landgirls with whom he worked in the threshing gang. This young lady, whose home was in Chichester, was new to the farming way of life, and yet like many another of her contemporaries soon became an inseparable part of it. The homely atmosphere of the farmhouse was also to weave its spell over her, resulting in a wedding taking place in that same village church in 1946. Their first home together was a small bungalow behind Poplar Hall, no more than half a mile from the farmstead from where as aforementioned he expanded the contracting business.

Following the death of Grandfather, and the necessity to administer his estate, the Harvey Farm was eventually sold, the family leaving at the end of July 1969. This was a sad blow but nevertheless one that had to be faced. After an occupation by the family for more than half a century, this farm, these buildings and especially that farmhouse were no longer to be alive with the chatter of this family of mine. No longer could we or any of us think of it or refer to it as home, and yet it was and still is able to hold a special place in our affections, for had it not housed us and supported us throughout one of the most significant eras of farming — the era of the steam engine? A few months after this sale had taken place Uncle Ron was able to purchase Parish Farm, Brookland not more than three-quarters of a mile from the Harvey and, save for a few willow trees, almost in sight of his former home; little of which remains save the farmhouse, stable and barn, to remind us of its former self. There he has been able to build up a large and most successful contracting business, using the most modern of today's farming methods and machinery. He and his men range far and wide as they go about their tasks. Not only the community upon the Marsh are familiar with the sight of his machinery, but farms and villages many miles away, out beyond the Military Canal and the market town of Ashford, regularly witness his comings and goings. His modern implements are today as familiar a sight as the family's steam engines were in their heyday.

One of his regular large customers is the farmer who bought the Harvey Farm who by that time also lived in the nearby Poplar Hall. This gentleman soon set about altering the face of his newest acquisition, in his desire to turn this property into one with the appearance of a parkland setting, being as it was in the view from his magnificent home. Most of the buildings were quickly demolished with the exception of the large barn and farmhouse. The former was skilfully converted into a stable block and the latter carefully screened from the road by the judicious planting of trees. New post and rail fences completed the scene to his satisfaction; but sadly for my part. The Harvey as we knew it no longer exists.

During the demolition of the old forge, undertaken by Uncle Ron and his men for the new owner, an important discovery was made. The chimney of the forge rose up as they were wont to do by steps of brickwork. Laying along some of these steps and covered like everything else around in soot and the dust of ages past the men found a few brass name plates, taken from the engines at some date prior to their being cut up.

Knowing of my own connection with the present day steam preservation movement and of my abiding interest in the family's history of steam, together with my setting down this work — he gave them to me. A gesture of great kindness on his part, for they are now amongst my most treasured possessions.

And so it is that to this day the Newton family continue to play their part in the lives of the agricultural community. Farms are visited today and land worked by Uncle Ron and his men that have been tended by my family for almost a hundred years. What yeoman service this has been and one of which I am justifiably proud. No longer may the steam ploughing engine be supreme but I am confident that my father, his father and his father before him, would all be satisfied to know that what each in his turn had striven so hard to achieve was still to this day continuing and in the charge of such a capable pair of hands.

For my part I have tried as best I can to record faithfully a little of what took place down those years, and some of the trials and tribulations that had to be faced each in their turn. Still the urge and spell of steam carries on through the family. I delight in being the owner of a fine Fowler Ploughing engine No. 14378 built in 1916, a B.B. compound machine one of the large collection of the late T.B. Paisley of Holywell in Huntingdonshire. Much work remains to be carried out on this engine to return it to its former glory. One thing about which I am certain, however, is the name that I have bestowed upon this mechanical masterpiece. As a lasting tribute to, and as a permanent reminder of, that great man of steam who happened also to be my grandfather I am having a brass nameplate made bearing the legend 'Wittersham Boy'.

Chapter 21

THE SCRAPMAN COMETH

The final days of the part played by my family in the use of steam engines commercially reads like a two act drama. The first scrap metal dealers to carry off some of these old redundant pieces of equipment came to the Harvey Farm early in 1939. The firm was Parkers of Portslade near Brighton. On this occasion, three ploughing engines were cut up, the pair Nos. 1904 and 1909 of 1873 and another from an 1870 pair No. 1437. At the same time the venerable old Wallis was reduced to scrap as was an old anti-balance plough body, which had been stripped for parts. The men from Parkers were at the Harvey for a few days, the payment being £25 per 10 ton engine.

It was during this work that Grandfather made a remark that seemed afterwards to have had a prophetic ring about it. Talking to one of the men engaged in this work he asked casually what was going to happen to the scrap iron upon its return to their yard. He was informed that it was going for export — to Germany! Obviously by this time dark murmurings were going on across the continent, and possibly being aware of some of its portent Grandfather said "You send my old engines over there as scrap, before long they will be sending them back as bombs"!

The war that soon followed resulted in a great number of steam engines surviving for many more years to come. Had it not been for the need for home food production many more would have gone the same way as those early loads to Portslade. Steam ploughing received its final shot in the arm during the years of this second global conflict. Threshing engines, like the Ruston at the Harvey, were again put to good use. The contemporary preservation scene owes much of its source of steam equipment to those same dismal years.

The final clearance of the remainder of the family's steam equipment came in the autumn of 1952. Everything remaining at that time was cut up on the spot by Lynch of Strood, near Rochester. Even the old Aveling was cut up where it stood on a piece of waste ground at Snargate a few miles from Brookland. The weighbridge tickets relating to these several loads of scrap iron existed until relatively recent times and showed a total weight of just over a 100 tons realising a figure of £480.

This time however, Uncle Ron was of an age to clearly remember what happened. He told me that three men came daily to the farm equipped not only with their acetylene torches but a tripod. Their method was to start at the top of an engine and cut it away letting it fall to the ground. Large lumps, weighing up

Opposite: Fowler No. 1199 14th June 1870 12 NHP single. Photo taken by D. Chamberlain circa 1944, after engine had been purchased by British Gates of Biddenden and partially dismantled. Kent County Council licence plate No. 211 clearly visible.

Fowler No. 3365 2nd November 1877 8 NHP. This photo clearly shows the odd rear wheel straking, referred to on page 75 — Photo taken by G. Eastes on 9th September 1951.
(Copy courtesy of B.D. Stoyel)

Fowler No. 3197 2nd October 1877 8 NHP. Like its mate this engine survived to the end of the Firm. — Photo taken by G. Eastes on 9th September 1951. (Copy courtesy of B.D. Stoyel)

to say 5cwt, they lifted aloft using block and tackle and then backed their lorry under them. Each day they cut up enough to make a lorry load, the whole job in hand lasting around three weeks. Yet these engines did not give up the struggle to survive easily — some even having to be winched from their resting places of many years beside the trackway now made muddy by the scrapmen's activities. They were winched by Uncle Ron using his Fordson tractor, thus equipped for its threshing duties — the ignominy of it all — to the roadside where they finally succumbed.

An interesting tale concerns the demise of engine No. 1199, one of the first 12hp pairs to have been owned by the family. Having lain idle for a good many years it was purchased by a firm, British Gates of Bethersden, Kent for £45. They wanted the boiler as a steam raising plant, presumably for steam bending — or possibly for drying timber. However they stripped the lagging from the engine and cut the rear wheels off, then called in the boilerman, who came and tested it, drilling a hole below the clack box — whereupon he condemned it. It was then cut up by Lynch of Strood with the others. "Father was paid twice for that old engine," said Uncle Ron with a giggle.

Uncle Ron tells me that a large enamelled jug of tea was taken out for the men engaged in this task. As if in a defiant last stand, a piece of metal shot off one of the engines as it was being cut up, knocking the jug clean off its resting place, leaving a large patch of enamel missing where it had been struck.

I remember seeing on my next visit not a line of engines, but only a chimney from one of them, on top of the outside copper fire in the corner of the yard, used as a chimney to give draught to the fire when cooking up small potatoes, not fit to sell, for stock feed. Reflecting on all this I feel extremely sad, as in those few days of 1952 all that my great grandfather, my grandfather and, in his turn, my father together with his brothers and sisters had cherished so much was done away with.

Why my grandfather, a man respected today by preservationists and possibly more famous now than ever before should have in his failing years have allowed himself to be persuaded to have his beloved steam engines cut up, I will never know. He had fiercely hung onto these for many years even though their useful life had finished, scorning the ridicule of his neighbours for doing so. Yet at a time when the traction engine preservation movement was getting under way — the early races at Appleford started in 1950 — he finally succumbed. How I wish he had not, for here was not just a collection of steam engines, of various ages, but for me at least a living thread that stretched back through the generations of my family to link me and my family and those that follow after me with an age — the like of which we will never see again.

If, however, we consider the circumstances, Grandfather was becoming old and had no use for them. Likewise the engines were by now in a rough state and no member of the family was interested in them. They were all too busy running their own lives. Preservation had indeed begun but only in a tentative way, and those few early preservationists who were looking for engines were looking for sound ones in working order from the large stocks that lay around the county. Likewise also, £480 was more than a year's wages in 1952. Perhaps Grandfather should therefore be forgiven by those that follow after. Is not hindsight after all the cheapest commodity in the world?

Nevertheless, to have possessed now those same machines that my forbears had used during a period of change for the world — never to be equalled — would have made me rich indeed — rich not in monetary terms — present day values having no place whatsoever in my reasoning — but rich in all manner of ways. For here in one small firm's motive power lay an extraordinary array of steam engines, some, as already recorded, dating back to the 1870s, some having been rebuilt, re-boilered and so on and yet others so original that today they would have been unique. A few lorry loads of assorted iron put an end to all those dreams, and yet one item did survive — a steam cultivator. This was acquired by the Ministry and sent overseas to the ill-fated ground nut scheme. It was towed by tractor to the roadside, where it was loaded onto a lorry and taken to Ashford prior to being exported. Can it be that in some far distant land under a hot burning sun, a relic of my family's connection with the age of steam survives?

The three ploughing engine vans were not, however, cut up with the rest. One was towed out into an adjoining paddock as a playhouse for Aunt Sybil's daughter Jennifer, where it remained for a few years. Another became temporary home in the corner of Plat field for a gentleman of the road, Alfred Wood, known to all as Sweedy. The remaining one was taken away to Wittersham, to serve what purpose I know not. None however survived for many years.

TAILPIECE

Since researching material for this volume I have made an interesting discovery, one which I have not been able so far to prove conclusively, but one which nevertheless I am certain is correct. This concerns a reference to a W.E. Newton in the book 'Ploughing by Steam' by John Haining and Colin Tyler. On page 162, mention is made that this gentleman was one of the pioneers of mechanical digging machines in 1852. My father often told me that his grandfather had been one of the men responsible for devising the coiling gear on ploughing engines. This he had frequently heard mentioned by elders of his family. His information had obviously not been strictly correct, but the rumour had nevertheless been based on some matter of substance. The man referred to being not his grandfather Edward, but his great grandfather W.E.

It is known for a fact that Edward's father had possessed the initials W.E., these initials which with few alterations have been passed down through the family, my grandfather being W.E., my father W.E. and my brother in his turn W.E.M., all of whom were the eldest son of the eldest son.

If indeed this information is correct a fact which I am hoping to substantiate quite shortly, it has for me an amazing implication, this being that I am, therefore, the fifth generation in my family to be a steam engine owner and my second son Barnaby who has already a share in an engine is the sixth.

This also means that our family has an unbroken link from generation to generation right through the era of the development of the steam engine in its application to agricultural use. This surely is one fact that not many families in the land can equal.

APPENDIX

From the records that exist and from detail given to me by others I have tried to establish certain facts relating to the engines owned and operated by my family. However some confusion still remains as the information gathered contains contradictions. Nevertheless, I append this below in the hope that it will be of some assistance to others in their researches.

Fowler 3197/3365 8hp single cylinder pair of 1877.
  This odd numbered pair were built on 2nd October 1877 and 2nd November 1877, respectively. Supplied new to John Body and Son of Wittersham. Sold together with all their tackle for £675 to E. Newton on 6th July 1891, payment being made by instalments finishing on 11th October 1895. No. 3197 was licensed by Kent County Council in 1921 as KE 6250, and it is presumed No. 3365 was KE 6251. Both engines were re-boilered using an Oxford Steam Plough Co. boiler during 1919/1920.
  Both survived until 1952 and they were scrapped by Lynch of Strood.

Fowler 1199/1200 12hp single cylinder pair of 1870 (10½" bore).
  Supplied new on 14th June 1870 to R.J. Sankey of Ashford being their No. 1 set and subsequently to G.R. Harnett of Birchington. No. 1199 was right hand engine, tank steerage, friction band wheels. Both engines were re-boilered using Oxford Steam Plough boilers.
  No. 1199 was also supplied with Kent County Council registration plate No. 211.
  Both engines were scrapped by Lynch of Strood in the autumn of 1952.

Fowler 1437/1438 12hp single cylinder pair of 1870 (10½" bore)
Supplied new on 17th October 1870 to R.J. Sankey of Ashford being their No. 2 set. Fowler's records state that 1438 was originally delivered in August 1870.
No. 1437 was scrapped by Parkers of Portslade in 1939 and No. 1438 by Lynch of Strood in 1952.

Fowler 1904/1909 12hp single cylinder pair of 1873.
Supplied new in May 1873 to the Bowling Iron Co. of Bradford. Subsequently to G. Henbrey. By 1916 to Newton of Brookland. However some confusion seems to exist in Fowler's records as 1909 is dubious. It appears from the records to have been a hauling engine and to have actually been Fowler 1792 May 1872 carrying a false No. 1909 plate.
Both engines scrapped by Parkers of Portslade in 1939.

Wallis and Steevens traction engine No. T.164 of 1882 6nhp single cylinder.
Licensed by West Sussex County Council as BP 6299. Supplied new on 5th August 1882 to Joseph Standing of Charlwood. Subsequently to Benjamin Chart of Horley, Surrey. Passing through two other changes of ownership before arriving at Brookland.
Scrapped by Parkers of Portslade in 1939.

Aveling and Porter traction engine No. 3069 6nhp single cylinder No. KE 6690.
Supplied new on 13th August 1892 to J. Cox of Egham. Subsequently to Henry Coombs of Bagshot on 27th February 1899, then to J. Palmer of Appledore. Painted in green, lined in red, dark green and cream. Carried a plate stating 7 tons. In reality it weighed when new 8 tons 9 cwt 1 qtr. Allotted County registration plate No. 176. Known as 'Tommy'.
Scrapped by Lynch of Strood in 1952.

Ruston Proctor traction engine No. 32404 1907 8nhp single cylinder.
Licence No. issued by Kent County Council in 1921 KE 6254. Painted blue. Supplied new to J. Higgins and Co. of Bonnington on 11th July 1907. Subsequently to Pains of Lydd.
Scrapped by Lynch of Strood in October 1952.